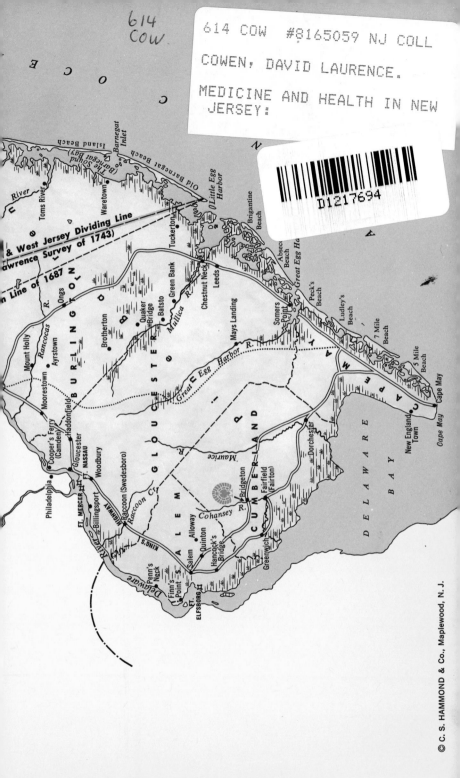

*Medicine and Health
in New Jersey: A History*

THE NEW JERSEY HISTORICAL SERIES

Edited by

RICHARD M. HUBER WHEATON J. LANE

Volume 16

The New Jersey Historical Series

Medicine and Health

in New Jersey: A History

DAVID L. COWEN

1964

D. VAN NOSTRAND COMPANY, INC.

Princeton, New Jersey

New York, N. Y. • Toronto, Canada • London, England

D. VAN NOSTRAND COMPANY, INC.
120 Alexander St., Princeton, New Jersey (*Principal office*)
24 West 40 Street, New York 18, New York

D. VAN NOSTRAND COMPANY, LTD.
358, Kensington High Street, London, W.14, England

D. VAN NOSTRAND COMPANY (*Canada*), LTD.
25 Hollinger Road, Toronto 16, Canada

Published simultaneously in Canada by
D. VAN NOSTRAND COMPANY (Canada), LTD.

PRINTED IN THE UNITED STATES OF AMERICA

To

The Memory of

MAE

FOREWORD

Many tracks will be left by the New Jersey Tercentenary celebration, but few will be larger than those made by the New Jersey Historical Series. The Series is a monumental publishing project—the product of a remarkable collaborative effort between public and private enterprise.

New Jersey has needed a series of books about itself. The 300th anniversary of the State is a fitting time to publish such a series. It is to the credit of the State's Tercentenary Commission that this series has been created.

In an enterprise of such scope, there must be many contributors. Each of these must give considerably of himself if the enterprise is to succeed. The New Jersey Historical Series, the most ambitious publishing venture ever undertaken about a state, was conceived by a committee of Jerseymen—Julian P. Boyd, Wesley Frank Craven, John T. Cunningham, David S. Davies, and Richard P. McCormick. Not only did these men outline the need for such an historic venture; they also aided in the selection of the editors of the series.

Both jobs were well done. The volumes speak for themselves. The devoted and scholarly services of Richard M. Huber and Wheaton J. Lane, the editors, are a part of every book in the series. The editors have been aided in their work by two fine assistants, Elizabeth Jackson Holland and Bertha DeGraw Miller.

To D. Van Nostrand Company, Inc. my special thanks for recognizing New Jersey's need and for bringing their skills and publishing wisdom to bear upon the printing and distributing of the New Jersey Historical Series.

My final and most heartfelt thanks must go to David L. Cowen, who accepted my invitation to write *Medicine and Health in New Jersey: A History,* doing so at great personal sacrifice and without thought of material gain. We are richer by his scholarship. We welcome this important contribution to an understanding of our State.

RICHARD J. HUGHES
*Governor of the
State of New Jersey*

January, 1964

PREFACE

Stephen Wickes' volume on the history of medicine in New Jersey was published eighty-five years ago. Wickes stopped his story at 1800 and his "history" was largely composed of biographical sketches. It is therefore appropriate that a new history of medicine in the State be included in the Tercentenary Series. To write a history of three hundred years of medicine in a small volume that would meet the editorial requirements of the Series, however, seemed a most difficult if not an impossible task. Yet the attempt needed to be made.

The brevity of the book was maintained partly by not multiplying the number of illustrations and partly by omitting or reducing subject matter where this could be done without undermining the total structure. Thus extended discussions of dentistry, pharmacy, and the pharmaceutical industry were eliminated, and other gaps, so obvious to an author, were left unfilled.

This book has been written mainly as a contribution to the history of medicine. Parochial interests, it will be clear, have not been disregarded, but the New Jersey experience may serve to point up the fact that the history of medicine includes the medicine that was practiced as a daily routine as well as the medicine that was scientifically explored and taught at great medical centers.

There remains a great deal of basic research to be done and a great deal more to be written about the history of medicine and health in New Jersey. Perhaps this small volume will call attention to the potentialities that exist for such research and writing.

The nineteenth century has received the greatest

amount of attention in the book. This is partly because the materials, quantitatively and qualitatively, are relatively scant for the earlier centuries and overly abundant for this century. The nineteenth century was not only a transition from the old to the new medicine; it was a formative period in which the basic groundwork for modern scientific medicine was laid.

A nineteenth-century New Jersey physician once likened New Jersey to a barrel with spigots at both ends that drained off its substance into New York and Philadelphia. The history of medicine and health reminds us that there was a two-way flow through these spigots—there is much our neighbors sent in our direction, from epidemics to medical school graduates.

My son, Bruce R. Cowen, M.D., and my colleagues, Dean G. Stuart Demarest and Abraham Yeselson, labored diligently with me in the early stages of the preparation of the manuscript and I am grateful to each of them for their criticism and advice. At the invitation of the editors of this Series, John B. Blake, John Duffy, Lester S. King, M.D., Fred B. Rogers, M.D., and Morris H. Saffron, M.D., each read the preliminary draft of the book. The exceptionally painstaking and thorough manner in which each subjected it to criticism, is a tribute to their sense of scholarly cooperation, and I hope, a mark of their personal friendship for me. I acknowledge a very considerable debt to them.

To the editors of this Series, Richard M. Huber and Wheaton J. Lane, I must also express my gratitude for wise counsel and extraordinary patience.

Many librarians have been of immeasurable assistance, particularly the staff of the Rutgers University Library. Donald A. Sinclair, Curator of Special Collections at Rutgers, gave me unsparingly of his time and advice. His amazing command of New Jersey bibliography and resources, and his comprehensive card file of New Jersey biographies saved me much time and energy. My debt to him is very great.

I must also express appreciation to Joseph Held for research assistance, and to Misses June Johnson and Marianne Zaabadick for their secretarial excellence, their ability to decipher my handwriting, and their good humor.

Finally, I wish to acknowledge with gratitude the assistance of the Rutgers Research Council which provided a semester's Rutgers Faculty Research Fellowship and other support.

DAVID L. COWEN

New Brunswick, New Jersey
March, 1964

TABLE OF CONTENTS

LIST OF ILLUSTRATIONS

I

THE SEVENTEENTH AND EIGHTEENTH CENTURIES

Y OU WILL FIND in all the Letters come from *Jersey,* this one particular specially marked, *That it is a very health-full Air;* no complaints of sickness there." Thus the promotional literature of the 1680's sought to induce settlers to come to the Jerseys.

How these letters managed to be concentrated in the hands of the publicists it is difficult to say, but there is no doubt of the agreement of a goodly number of correspondents—or the consistency of the copywriter—on the salubrity of the air and the healthfulness of the climate. "The *Air* of this *Province* is very Serene, Sweet, and Wholesome," wrote one settler, "which renders the *Clime* much more agreeable to *European* Bodies than the severe Colds of *New England,* or the sulphurous Heat in *Virginia;* where, I say, the Bogs, Marshes, and corrupt Standing-Waters, have ever been very Noxious to the Planter." It was even hinted that death had come to "the greatest part" who went to Carolina, the province that was at the moment the chief competitor of the Jerseys for settlers.

In so healthy a region as that pictured by the letter writers of the 1680's there should have been little to entice the medical profession. Indeed, in 1685 Charles Gordon of Woodbridge wrote to his brother Dr. John Gordon in Scotland as follows:

If you design to come hither your self, you may come as a

Planter, or a *Merchant,* but as a *Doctor* of Medicine I cannot
advise you; for I hear of no diseases here to cure but some
Agues, and some cutted legs and fingers; and there are no
want of *Empiricks* for these already; I confess you could doe
more than any yet in *America,* being versed both in *Chirur-
gery, Pharmacie,* for here are abundance of curious Herbs,
Shrubs, and Trees, and no doubt *Mediciniall* ones for making
of drogs; but there is little or no Imployment in this way. . . .

DISEASE IN COLONIAL NEW JERSEY

But the vision of the letter writers was undoubtedly
blurred, for both before and after their praises appeared
in print illness had visited the province. Indeed New
Jersey during the colonial period (and into the nineteenth century, too) seemed almost constantly ravaged by
one or another of the infectious diseases.

The first known attack of disease in the province occurred in 1642 when the Swedes and English at Salem
Creek were struck by a malady that almost "dissolved"
the settlement of the latter. The first identified malady,
malaria, was noted at the end of the seventeenth century.
Measles appeared in 1713 and was "mortal" in Salem the
next year. Smallpox began a seven-year rampage in 1715
and was reported in Burlington even before Philadelphia
and New York. It returned to New Jersey in at least four
epidemics in the eighteenth century. Diphtheria and
scarlet fever hit New Jersey in 1735-1736, but both were
to do their most horrible work in the next century.
Yellow fever came to Burlington in 1743, and New Jersey
probably never escaped its scourge each time New York
or Philadelphia was infected. Respiratory diseases were
rampant enough to be reported five times in the century,
and "bilious fever" and typhoid fever were also reported.
"Fever" and "agues" were at times said to be "universal."

With regard to such diseases, however, New Jersey was
not completely helpless. Feeble attempts were made at
quarantine, as when Burlington prohibited all fairs in
1731 "by reason of the great Mortality in *Philadelphia,*
and other Parts of *Pennsylvania,* where the Small-Pox

now violently Rages." The same measures were taken by Salem County officials at that time and again in 1737. More significant was variolation—inoculation with small-pox virus—which gained some attention in New Jersey in 1759 when the Reverend Colin Campbell, Anglican missionary in Burlington, inoculated his own children as an example. Dr. William Barnet, of Elizabethtown, was invited to Philadelphia in 1759 to inoculate for the small-pox. In 1760, "Americanus," writing in the *Pennsylvania Journal,* claimed that in New Jersey thousands of lives had been saved by the "new method of treating those under Inoculation" (with calomel and diaphoretic antimony). Americanus claimed that only one out of seven hundred died and only one in one hundred got the full disease, "while in the common way of Infection, 1 dies out of 5." This is probably the earliest such use of medical statistics in New Jersey.

DOMESTIC MEDICINE

The colonial New Jerseyman, almost by necessity at first because of the scarcity of medical practitioners, was just as given to self-medication as is his modern counterpart. The Jersey housewife was, and indeed had to be, the first resort in case of illness in her family. Household receipt books, carefully copied in the hand of the mistress of the house, testify to this basic reliance upon domestic medicine.

The medicine practiced in the home was in part folk medicine, some of it perhaps learned from the Indians, and in part borrowed from authoritative or presumed-authoritative sources. The commonplace book of the Hankinson family of Reading, New Jersey, begun about 1787, was typical. It contained, among sundry "infallible," "efectual," and "Indian Squaw's" cures, receipts like the following:

to Raise a blister
take Buternut Bark from the North Side of the Tree near

the Rute as Large a peace as you wish the Blister to be [.]
Shave the outside off [.] Lay it in Vinegar one half hour or
Longer [.] apply it, if not likely to Raise a Blister wet it a
second time and apply [.]

The housewife might also have at her disposal an herb
garden in which medicinal "simples" were raised. How
many of these were indigenous and how many the settlers
had learned about from the Indians it is impossible to
say. Ginseng was apparently known locally and Virginia
snakeroot became popular in the eighteenth century. The
eventual appearance of *Ceanothus americanus*—a plant
that bears the common name "New Jersey Tea" and was
purportedly used as a substitute for Chinese tea during
the Revolution—in the pharmacopoeias of the nineteenth
century, bears evidence of the use of local plants in
medicine.

For her medical knowledge the housewife could go to
a variety of sources. The newspapers did not hesitate to
inform her about reportedly successful remedies. When
The New-York Weekly Journal reported (February 9,
1735/6) the occurrence of "throat distemper" at Crosswicks, it also recommended a gargle made with honey,
the sharpest vinegar, and alum. For children, the same
mixture was to be swabbed on the throat with a feather.

Almanacs also offered gratuitous medical advice. Tim-
othy Trueman's *The Burlington Almanack for . . . 1771*
contained an eight-page extract of hints from a "Treatise
on Health." Receipts were not uncommon in such publications; sometimes, however, they required an access to
crude drugs and a knowledge of compounding beyond the
capacity of the average reader. Sometimes, too, a single
receipt was recommended for an unbelievable array of
illnesses.*

There were also numerous medical handbooks avail-

* See for example, the complicated receipt attributed to Dr. E.
Watkinson and good for costiveness, whooping cough, convulsive
fits, worms, and a host of other conditions, in *The Burlington Almanack for . . . 1774.*

able to the layman, an increasing number of them published in the colonies. John Wesley's rather aptly named *Primitive Physic* went through at least seven printings in America between 1764 and 1795, including one at Trenton in 1788.

Early in the eighteenth century, moreover, a great variety of British "patent medicines" began to come to the aid of the housewife, and these were ordinarily available in drug and country stores. By 1779, G. Duyckinck of Morristown advertised a complete line of such remedies, including Anderson's Pills (a mild purgative), Bateman's Drops (a specific for a multitude of illnesses), Daffy's Elixir (or "Health-Bringing Drink"), and Hooper's Female Pills.

The Practitioner and His Training

Folk medicine and home remedies have obvious limitations, and, despite the idyllic image of New Jersey in the early propaganda, it was soon evident that practitioners of medicine had a place in the colony. There is record of no fewer than twenty practitioners of medicine in New Jersey in the seventeenth century, and although few of them could devote themselves entirely to the practice of physic, all but three of these migrants practiced professionally.

Thus in the 1670's "Dr." Henry Greenland practiced in Woodbridge and sundry other Middlesex locations; Charles Haynes was a "surgeon" at Middletown; Bernard Devonish a "barber surgeon" at New Salem; and Daniel Wills a "practitioner in chymestry" and "Dr. of Physsick" at Northampton. In the next two decades three of the arrivals were styled "Doctor of Physick," two were "practitioner of medicine," one was "physician," one a "practitioner of physic and surgery," four were "surgeons," one an "apothecary," and three others were practitioners without designation.

This variety of "medical" men followed the pattern of

practice in the British Isles. All sooner or later became general practitioners of medicine. John Johnstone was "apothecary" en route to America, but after arrival "Doctor"—probably given the title in the popular English fashion of the time which used that appellation for all practitioners. Indeed, there were among these seventeenth-century New Jersey practitioners none to whose name the M.D. seems to have ever been attached, for conditions could hardly have been better on the Jersey frontier than they were in the home country.

In the American colonies the responsibility for caring for the settlers' health often fell to the political and religious leaders of the community. They were the educated and literate group, often with some interest in science, and perhaps also with some medical training. In New Jersey we find no counterpart of Governor John Winthrop, but the "angelic conjunction" between the ministry and physic was not only common but accepted by the medical profession. Oddly there is no direct evidence of this conjunction in the seventeenth century,* but in the eighteenth we find some outstanding examples. The Reverend Mr. Jonathan Dickinson, first president of the College of New Jersey, practiced medicine and ministered spiritually to his flock at Elizabethtown; the first president of the New Jersey Medical Society in 1766 was the Reverend Robert McKean of Perth Amboy. In the first ten years of the Medical Society, six of its 36 members were pastor-physicians. There seems to have been little objection from the profession about clerical competition; the clergy needed other means of support, just as the physicians also sought other means of procuring income. Indeed the complaints about the joining of the two professions came from another direction entirely—the parishioner-patients. They felt embarrassed in settling accounts with their own minister and believed that the practice of physic interfered with the duty of a clergyman. The "greatest part of the congregation" of the Anglican

* Wickes could find no evidence that the Reverend Abraham Pierson practiced medicine.

≈§ 6 §≈

Church at Perth Amboy rejected the Reverend Isaac Brown in 1769 on these grounds.

For such reasons, and because of a growing secularization of society and the growing educational and professional demands of medical practice, a "distinction between physic and divinity" began to develop where there had been little before. In any event, by 1796 the membership list of the Medical Society had reached a total of 91, among whom numbered only seven clergymen. Out of the last 55 to join the Society by that year, only one was a clergyman.

In New Jersey none of the restrictions on medical practice prevailing in England (and very loosely enforced there) was in effect. Thus there were many "physicians by instinct," men or women of inclination and impudence who set themselves up as practitioners of medicine, with no training, with or without the guidance of some semi-professional handbook like Nicholas Culpeper's *English Physician*. Most practitioners, however, learned the trade through apprenticeship. This was the normal procedure by which the New Jersey physician received his training, not only throughout the colonial period, but well down into the nineteenth century.

Apprenticeship might vary in length of service. There was no general agreement as to how long it should be, and the New Jersey Medical Society, when it discussed the matter in 1767, one year after its founding, agreed not to accept an apprentice for less than four years, although one of these four could be spent at a school of medicine. It is evident, however, that the time of service was never regularized—witness the certificate given to John Kaighim to the effect that he had served for "a considerable time."

As the eighteenth century progressed, there were practitioners who had received formal training to be found. New immigrants came to New Jersey claiming medical education in the schools abroad; several native New Jerseymen laid claim to having studied abroad; and a few other American-born physicians who had studied abroad set up practices in New Jersey. Most of these men claimed Edinburgh as the source of their training; others claimed London, Paris, Leyden, and Rheims, or more than one of these places. Of these Thomas Cadwalader, a New Jersey physician of the eighteenth century, has gained the most fame. Although he spent most of his professional life in Philadelphia, Cadwalader lived in Trenton, was its first "chief burgess," and practiced there for a while.

When medical schools opened in both Philadelphia and New York, Jerseymen took advantage of the opportunities. Among the first ten to receive the Bachelor of Medicine degree at the College of Philadelphia in 1768 were two Jerseymen: Jonathan Elmer and John Lawrence. (Elmer was awarded the Doctor of Medicine degree in 1771.) By 1800 New Jersey could boast at least ten men who had received medical degrees in Philadelphia and New York.

Were we to lump together all the practitioners who claimed foreign institutional training, the ten known American graduates from New Jersey, and seven others known to have attended some formal institution at either Philadelphia or New York, we would get a grand total of 41 medical men, out of approximately three hundred, in New Jersey before 1800 who could boast of some training beyond apprenticeship. New Jersey was not, however, particularly backward in this respect. It is estimated that of the thirty-five hundred established practitioners in all of the colonies before the Revolution, only four hundred had had formal training, and only about two hundred held medical degrees.*

There were attempts to promote further medical education in New Jersey. In 1752 Dr. Thomas Wood advertised a "course on Osteology and Myology" for one month, "to be followed (if encouraged) by a course in

* These figures are from Richard H. Shryock, *Medicine and Society in America* (New York, 1960), 9. Joseph M. Toner, *Contributions to the Annals of Medical Progress* (Washington, 1874), 106, places the number of degree holders at between three hundred and fifty and four hundred.

Angiology and Neurology," and concluding with "operations on the dead body." The courses were to be held at New Brunswick, but there is no record of Wood's ever having received sufficient encouragement for the continuation of his efforts. Similarly Paul Micheau attempted to start a one-man medical school at Elizabethtown in 1790 that offered one lecture daily for two months for twenty-five dollars tuition. He seems not to have progressed very far, succeeding mainly in being accused of starting an independent Medical Society of the Eastern District of New Jersey as a device for granting a Doctor of Medicine degree and attracting students. Attempts to start medical instruction at the college at Princeton in 1795 proved abortive, and the granting of medical degrees by Queen's College in the 1790's was merely an arrangement of convenience to Dr. Nicholas Romayne of New York, whereby his students, certified by him, were awarded the degree by the Queen's College authorities.

A prerequisite of medical education and research in the eighteenth century was anatomizing. George Gordon of "Amboy Perth" provided in his will of January 20, 1685/6 that "Dr. Robieson may dissect me." If Dr. Robieson (Robinson) did so, it was the first instance of dissection for anatomical study in New Jersey, and one of the earliest such investigations in the colonies.

In 1762 the body of a prisoner executed at Gloucester was ordered by the Chief Justice to be sent to Dr. Shippen's anatomical theater in Philadelphia. Permitted by common law, this procedure was given a statutory basis in New Jersey in 1796 following the lead of New York (1789) and the federal government (1790). There is also evidence that bodies had been exhumed from graves by anatomists without benefit of either common or statute law.

Individually, none of these attempts at education or anatomizing seems significant; together, however, they indicate, along with the increase in formal training of physicians, that the profession was maturing and attaining stature. This improvement resulted from greater study, knowledge, and speculation—if not from science. It is true that the cleric-physician, and the "Preacher-Teacher-Doctor-Proctor-Miller-Distiller" seem to have been found throughout New Jersey at the end of the eighteenth century, but the profession was beginning to feel a sense of professional identity. New Jersey was to be the first of the colonies to indicate this by the formation of a provincial medical society and the passage of a law requiring the licensing of physicians.

It is useless to speculate as to why New Jersey led the colonies in this early venture into organized medicine and the promulgation of a licensing law, for there is nothing to indicate that New Jersey was markedly different in a medical sense from other provinces in the North. Whatever the basis, in 1766 the New Jersey Medical Society was formed, and although its existence was not continuous, it is the only colonial society with a direct and flourishing descendant. (In 1790 it was incorporated as the Medical Society of New Jersey; it was known as the Medical Society of the State of New Jersey from 1816 to 1818; and called the Medical Society of New Jersey since then.)

The original minute-book of the New Jersey Medical Society opens with a reference to "The low state of Medicine in New Jersey." Because of it, "and the many difficulties and discouragements, alike injurious to the people and the physician," several members of the profession called a meeting for July 23, 1766, at New Brunswick. There, "for their mutual improvement, the advancement of the profession and the promotion of the public good," 14 "Practitioners of Physic and Surgery" formed the New Jersey Medical Society.

The activity of the Society in its early years indicated that these purposes were interpreted as meaning, first, the improvement of the economic status of the profession; second, the improvement of the professional status through the imposition of licensing requirements; and third, the dissemination of medical knowledge within the profession. All of these would limit competition, but all, it was always contended, would redound to the advantage of the public in providing competent and up-to-date practitioners.

The very first action taken by the Society at its first meeting, after the establishment of a constitution and the election of officers, was the preparation and discussion of "A Table of Fees and Rates." This oft-quoted fee bill was long and detailed, and projected a set of fairly substantial fees. However, there was to be no charge for one or two visits in town—the doctor, like the British apothecary, charging only for the medicines he dispensed. For cases requiring extended daily visits, the charge was to be ten shillings per week, exclusive of medicines. Visits outside of town were to be charged on the basis of mileage. A phlebotomy (blood-letting) or an extraction of a tooth would cost 1s.6d.

Operations varied in cost from 15s. for a finger to £5 for cutting for the stone. A charge was made for each post-operative dressing. Midwifery in a "natural case" was to cost £1 10s. and £3 in "preternatural cases." Medicines varied from a shilling per dose of an alterative powder to 7s. 6d. for a decoction containing one ounce of Peruvian bark.

The preamble of the bill is an interesting rationalization of the position of the practitioners. Theirs was a profession that required a great deal of sacrifice, that was constantly exposed to disease, that had many disagreeable tasks to perform, that required many "painful" years of training at great expense, and that therefore deserved "a just and equitable reward." The bill of fees was fair and did not increase the usual charges. It would prevent disputes between patient and physician, and would "obviate the impositions of quacks." The fees, too, were directed against the price-cutter, for although the individual member was to be permitted to "abate what part of such bills he may think proper, on account of poverty, friendship, or other laudable motives," he was "under pain of expulsion" if such abatement arose from any "other consideration whatever."

Four months after the first meeting the Society had to reconsider its fee table. The lesson of the need for good public relations was learned quickly. "Evil-minded persons had thrown an odium on the proceedings of this Society," lamented the minutes of the meeting of November 4, 1766, "tending to prejudice the minds of the inhabitants against so laudable an Institution." The Society had been accused of trying "to bring the inhabitants to terms." The obligation to follow the fee bill was therefore repealed, and the Society decided to mend its public-relations fences by the publication of a statement of its purpose and its constitution. Whether or not the fee bill was thereafter technically in effect is not clear, but not until 1810 was a new bill established.

"Medical Economics" was thus a concern of the profession from the very beginning of the organization in the State. But the Medical Society was soon concerned with other matters—the education and qualifications of the medical practitioner.

The almost immediate concern of the Society with the preparatory education of students of medicine has already been alluded to. For the "honor of the art," too, the Society, though anxious to expand its membership, politely rejected the applications of two practitioners, one (1767) without credentials, the other (1769) because he had been found by the Committee "deficient in some important branches of medical erudition." Moreover, the Society went to the length of expelling several members between 1771 and 1774, at least three for non-attendance, and one for being "a person really scandalous."

The major activity directed toward the elevation of the professional status of the practitioners, however, was that directed toward the licensing of physicians. Here indeed the New Jersey Society was moving in new directions for British North America, for only New York had a statute of this kind. It had been passed in 1760, but was applicable, however, only to the City of New York. In the home country sporadic attempts at licensing and enforcement of licensing laws seemed to interfere little with the fluidity of medical practice. In the colonies, the Massachusetts General Court had made some vague motions toward licensing in the seventeenth century. Elsewhere there had been a few scattered examples of the licensing of practitioners—the General Court of Rhode Island granted a license in 1663 and the Connecticut legislature granted three between 1686 and 1717.

In New Jersey there were also instances of early licensure. In March, 1705/6 the Lieutenant Governor issued a license from Burlington to Richard Smith, and a few months later, the Governor issued one to Nathaniel Wade.* These licenses were in the nature of an honor which did not limit the rights of others, and were not issued to meet statutory requirements. Presumably they implied that the licensee possessed professional competence, as Smith's license indicates:

> To Richard Smith Gentleman Greeting
> Being well Informed of your Knowledg, Skill and Judgment in the practice of Chirurgery & Phisig, I do hereby Lycence and Authorise You to practice the Said Sciences of Chirurgery and Physig within this her Majestys Province of New Jersey for and Dureing Pleasure. . . .
> > Rich: Ingolsby

At its 1768 meeting the Medical Society appointed a committee to prepare a petition to the provincial legislature "to obtain a law to regulate the practise of physic and surgery in this Province." The medical profession in New Jersey, finding inadequate the organization and dis-

---

* One of the Connecticut licensees (1695) was also a Nathaniel Wade and this may well have been the same man.

cipline it had developed—itself unusual if not unique in the colonies—thus sought the assistance of governmental authority. A flow of petitions followed. There are copies of two of these still in existence, both originating in the Freehold area, one with five and the other with 106 signatures. Both requested Governor William Franklin to reduce the "Profession of a Physician or Surgeon . . . to . . . a Standard or certainty with regard to his knowledge, capacity and ability," and to examine and regulate the profession.

The desired end was finally attained in 1772, and New Jersey became the first of the colonies to establish a provincial system of examination and licensing of physicians. Thereafter—the act exempted anyone already in practice —a license to practice as a physician or surgeon required an examination, approval, and admission to practice, by two judges of the Supreme Court with the assistance of "such proper Person or Persons as they in their Discretion shall think fit."

MEDICAL "SCIENCE"

In still another way—and this perhaps the most significant of all—did the New Jersey Society seek to elevate the profession: the exchange of medical information and opinions, the presentation of cases, the discussion of therapeutics, and the general promotion of interest in the medical science of the day. Indeed, in New Jersey, where medical research was not to develop for a long time, such exchange of information was the science of the day; at least it was a program of continuing education to which the professional practitioner was initiate and the empiric was not.

Early in its history the Society instituted the requirement that the meetings be opened by the President with a discourse "upon some medical subject." After 1790 each member was required to read a paper or present a case for discussion. It is, in fact, quite evident that "learned discussion" was the eighteenth century's device to overcome the scientific shortcomings of the age in medicine.* Since scientific proof in the modern sense was not within the ken of the profession, the weight of opinion became significant, and we find the Society deciding medical questions by vote. Thus, when the Society had before it, in 1789, the questions of the causes and cure of dysentery, "A question was at length taken on the proximate cause of dysentery, and carried in favor of spasm."

The caliber of the presentations also reflected the limitations of the time. At the second meeting of the Society in 1766 the President communicated the recipe for a stomachic electuary, a "nostrum of the late Doctor Jared Elliott [sic] of Connecticut," the chief ingredient of which was powdered glass. The dosage of this electuary was to be determined by the patient's reaction. If sufficient, the patient "would instantly [feel] a very strong pungent pain, and an universal shock . . . particularly extending itself to the extremities." If this did not occur, "the dose should then be increased till those sensations were produced"! To the credit of the assembled group, the Society was reported as "greatly surprised at the accounts, but judged it not prudent to recommend the use of it, without some authentic proof of its success." The recipe was, however, "permitted to be inserted in the Society's book."

Much more characteristic—and by no means only in New Jersey—was the need to resort to description and tautology where the medical science was inadequate to explain causes. "By a dropsy," declared President Elisha Newell in 1795, "I understood the preternatural collection of serous or watery fluids, in one or more parts of the body, in consequence of an increased effusion, or diminished absorption, or both."

* "It would be unjust to expect very much from medicine in the American colonies at a time when there was much left to be desired in Europe . . ."—Henry E. Sigerist, *American Medicine* (New York, 1934), 31.

Broadside of the apothecary, Robert Talbot, c. 1725, one of the earliest American medical imprints

If the medical "science" of the colonial American practitioner seemed primitive, it must be remembered that
this was at a time when the leaders of the medical profession in Europe could not agree on fundamental principles. A great many ideological influences were at work
in the medical world of the eighteenth century, some new,
some old, and even in the remote province of New Jersey
their impact was to be felt.

Thomas Sydenham, "The British Hippocrates" of the
seventeenth century, was most directly influential in
eighteenth-century New Jersey. His books were to be
found on the shelves of Jersey physicians and he was
exalted, by the President of the Medical Society of New
Jersey in 1787, as the founder of "modern" medical
knowledge.

Sydenham thought of disease as an entity whose nature
and symptoms could be learned by clinical study: disease
had an existence separate from the particular patient.
This "ontological conception," which departed widely
from the then current notion of the inseparable connection between the patient and the disease, may not have
had any appreciable intellectual impact on the mind of
the New Jersey practitioner of the late eighteenth century, but Sydenham's "common sense," his close observation, his skeptical and empirical attitudes, his interest in
diseases rather than in theories, must have given encouragement, if not a sense of scientific support, to the New
Jersey practitioner faced with the problem of getting
practical results as soon as possible. Sometimes, it must be
added, Sydenham's approach did not always serve to
clarify: "Diseases sometimes put on so many different
appearances," said his Jersey disciple, William Burnet in
1787, "their symptoms are so varied and equivocal, so
complex and intermixed, that it is enough to puzzle the
most watchful, sagacious observer."

Sydenham was but one of the influences at work in
New Jersey medicine. The school of iatrochemists of the

seventeenth century, whose ideological ancestor was the renowned Paracelsus, saw the body as a chemical laboratory, and disease in terms of excessive acidity or alkalinity. Out of this came a therapeutics which outlasted the theory: mineral and chemical materia medica that became and remained a large part of the armamentarium of medical men. That this influence was at work in eightenth-century New Jersey is also clear: Robert Talbot, apothecary and chemist of Burlington, stocked along with the usual great variety of vegetable medicinals, the minerals, chemicals, elixirs, and tinctures that were required by the post-Paracelsian school of therapeutics.

Still older influences, moldy with tradition, were also to be found in New Jersey. Talbot's list of drugs, published as a broadside about the time of his death in 1725, the earliest separate publication by a pharmacist in the colonies, is replete not only with the vegetable simples that went back to Galen and Dioscorides, but also with much of the ancient and medieval polypharmaceuticals and other claptrap that still cluttered the materia medica of the day. Thus there were available to the practitioners of Burlington—as to their counterparts in London, Amsterdam, or Paris—mithridatum, dioscoridum, and Venice treacle; sealed earth, bezoar stone, musk, hartshorn, and "crabs eyes." Missing from Talbot's list, it should be noted, were most of the vile animal parts and excrements that were all still official in the European pharmacopoeias.

And finally, still a fourth influence was at work on the practice of medicine in New Jersey. Galen, Paracelsus, and Sydenham—and other respectable authors whose works were found in the libraries of physicians—had to share their honors with writers of popular medical works —some intended for the practitioner, some for the layman, but both undoubtedly used by the physicians. The estate of Dr. John DeWildey of Salem County, for example, who died in 1707, included Culpeper's *Dispensatory* and *English Physician* and Johnson's *Dispensatory*. Dr. John Roberts of Burlington had in his collection of 29 medical books Salmon's *London Dispensatory* and a supplement to it called *Phylaxa medicina,* and two editions of a work called "Good Housewife Made a Dr." These same two works by Salmon, and others by him, and Culpeper's *English Physician,* appeared again in the library of a Dr. Jonathan Smith, another Burlington physician, 25 years later in 1758. John Quincy's *Dispensatory,* a more professional work, and later William Buchan's extremely popular *Domestic Medicine,* a work written at a rather high level, were probably just as frequently used in New Jersey as they were elsewhere in the colonies.

There is a good deal that can be told about the actual practice of medicine in the eighteenth century in New Jersey. The physician seems to have done most of his work at the patient's bedside. His fees for visits varied according to the place and time. Visits in town "without riding" might not be charged for, other visits were charged on a mileage basis, visits at night called for a special fee, and visits *omne noct.* (all night), a still higher fee. The physician dispensed his own medicines which he carried with him, and undoubtedly derived the larger part of his income from them. His office equipment always included a mortar and pestle, balances, vials, bottles, salvatories (to hold ointments), and such.

His armamentarium was large and varied—reflecting the varied influences previously discussed. The neat records of Dr. Moses G. Elmer of New Providence, for example, indicate that in the course of treatment of a single patient (whose illness is not given) in 1786, there were administered sal ammoniac, cream of tartar, and an antimonial mixture, as well as cephalic, anti-spasmodic, purging, cathartic, emetic, and anodyne pills, boluses (large pill masses), powders, and guttera (compound powders). Only two vegetable drugs were named—valerian root prescribed both as a simple and as an elixir, and powdered jalap. But these medicaments were merely a portion of the treatment. Dr. Elmer's patient, one Ephraim Miller, who apparently lived to pay a bill of over £39, was also subjected to blood-letting no less than 14 times, and to blistering plasters, on his head and shoulders, 24 times in his three-month illness. Apparently too, a seton was applied and "continued many months." (A seton was an implant, usually a thread, placed under the skin at the nape of the neck, with its two ends hanging out. It created an "issue" or drainage.)

In 1784 when the same Dr. Elmer treated one Benjamin Force, he had used a still different variety of drugs, listing some by traditional names, as magnesia, paragoric, and spermaceti, and others by functional names. Mr. Force seems seldom to have been bled, but as his affliction became evidently venereal, he was given regular doses of powdered mercury and diuretic powder, and his legs and genitals were punctured and scarified, over an extended period, sometimes as a daily routine.

It is thus clear that the practitioner—and there is no reason to suspect that Dr. Elmer was atypical—knew little and cared less about medical theory and schools of medicine; he examined his patient and selected a therapeutic treatment that would perform the functions he believed were indicated. That he speculated in advance as to external or proximate causes, iatrochemistry, or iatrophysics (the school that thought of the body as a mechanism) is highly improbable.

From Galen he had learned to treat general body conditions—humors—with vegetable and animal remedies, with bleeding, and with purging and blistering; from Paracelsus he had learned about mercury and antimony; from Sydenham he had learned to look for specific diseases; and William Cullen had given him a functional concept of the materia medica based on a neat taxonomy. Dr. Elmer's practice was eclectic, and probably so from experience rather than from reason or choice.

The practitioner was likely to be just as frustrated at his failure to understand the causes and the cures of the constant stream of epidemic diseases that he encountered as were his professional descendants a century later. But his approach was empirical, in a rather *ad hominem*, practical, and pragmatic sort of way. This empiricism was hardly the scientific variety that called for careful observation and testing, nor was it the sheer charlatanry which earned quacks the sobriquet of "empirics." Perhaps the approach was most plainly stated at the end of pastor-physician Jonathan Dickinson's extended *Observations On that terrible Disease, Vulgarly called The Throat Distemper, With Advices as to the Method of Cure* (Boston, 1740). In this, probably the first professional medical work by a Jerseyman, after presenting a rather bewildering array of symptoms and variations upon them, and just as bewildering a variety of recommended medicines—Virginia snake root, squaw root, Gascoign powder, Venice treacle, laudanum, elixir proprietatis, calomel, etc.—Dickinson concluded by saying, "I have not attempted a *Philosophical* Inquiry into the Nature of this Disease, nor a *Rationale* upon the Methods of Cure. I have meant no more than briefly to communicate to you some of my *Experiences* in this Distemper. . . ."

The colonial practitioner was a truly general practitioner; there was little he might not be called upon to do. In addition to venesection (blood-letting), creating issues with the seton, and administering medicine, as noted for Ephraim Miller above, the practitioner might be required to extract teeth, cup and scarify, dress wounds, open abcesses, catheterize, administer an enema, inoculate for smallpox, reduce fractures, and deliver women in labor, using forceps or others instruments where required. Moreover, the practitioner was also surgeon, and on the Society's fee bill were listed such operations as trepanning, extraction of cataract, bronchotomy, "extirpation of the tonsils," operations for the "Hare-lip," and for the "Wry-neck," amputations of the limbs and breasts, "Hydrocle Radical operation," paracentesis, extirpation of tumors, and cutting for the stone, among others.

How many such operations the ordinary practitioner performed it is difficult to say, but there is little doubt that the country doctor was sometimes left with little alternative but to operate. In the country or the city, however, surgery, in an age which had neither asepsis nor antisepsis, and whose best available anesthetics were liquor and opium, left much to be desired. A boy who had a tumor extirpated from his arm before the Medical Society in 1785, had to have the arm amputated four days later, was the victim of lockjaw one week after that, and was ill for 17 weeks more.

The eighteenth century ended with only two outstanding accomplishments in medicine. One was the displacement of variolation by vaccination. This was the work of Edward Jenner and substituted for inoculation with smallpox virus inoculation with the milder cowpox virus. The other was the work of Giovanni Morgagni and emphasized the anatomic changes in particular organs that occurred in particular diseases; post-mortem findings and clinical records were being correlated.

Jenner's contribution was to have a tremendous effect, but for a long time the lessons learned from Morgagni did not give the physician any great new powers, except so far as surgery was concerned. Indeed, eighteenth-century European medicine, despite the earlier empirical approach of Sydenham, despite the scientific lessons taught by Morgagni, and despite the practical success of Jenner, developed new systems of medicine that were rational and theoretical rather than scientific or empirical.

Of the more recent theories which most affected America, and New Jersey, the source was William Cullen in Edinburgh. Cullen made nervous force and nerve tone the core of his diagnostic and therapeutic system. Another Scot, John Brown, a student of Cullen's, went on to develop the system that was to be called Brunonianism, in which disease was reduced to one of two conditions, excessive tension or excessive relaxation—"sthenic" and "asthenic" states. And it was Benjamin Rush, American, and another student of Cullen, who simplified the system still further. All disease was the consequence of a condition of excessive tension—of "irregular convulsive or wrong action" in the body.

Regardless of which of these theories was followed— and the early nineteenth-century practitioner mixed and matched the theories as he went improvisingly along—the therapeutics were not far different. For the atonic or asthenic conditions, stimulants and tonics were to be used. For the sthenic condition of the Brunonians, and the excessive tension of Rush, copious bleeding, usually accompanied by thorough purging, was the treatment.

In some measure the resort to theory reflected the absence of a truly scientific basis for the practice of medicine. Practice became a combination of adapting the case to the theory and of a rule-of-thumb kind of trial-and-error process. The dictum that the eighteenth-century practitioner in New York was "ignorant, degraded and contemptible" is perhaps too harsh, but it is difficult to find any substantial evidence that the New Jersey practitioner was to any appreciable extent critically empirical or scientifically factual about his work. This situation was to continue for almost all of the next century.

II

THE UNCERTAINTIES
OF MEDICINE
IN THE NINETEENTH CENTURY

THE PUBLISHED TRANSACTIONS of the Medical Society of
New Jersey include, for all of the nineteenth century,
annual reports from county correspondents. These, together with the summaries and editorial comment of the
"Standing Committee" of the Society, offer a significant
source of information on health and medical practice in
the State. For the most part these were grass-roots reports;
the correspondents were practical men, and theirs were
matter-of-fact reports of diseases, therapies, and the customary "unusual cases."

Indeed here was medicine as it was practiced; the
presidential addresses and the prepared papers presented
before the Medical Society reflected the medicine that was
preached. But whether it was the medicine that was
practiced or that which was preached, it is clear that
medicine of the nineteenth century, in New Jersey as elsewhere, was severely limited in its effectiveness. Up until
virtually the last decade of the century, the record in New
Jersey—which perhaps offers a more realistic account of
the history of the practice of medicine than the accounts
of academic medicine and brilliant new achievements in
the medical centers of the world—indicates the dualistic
character of medicine. There was knowledge and there
was ignorance, there was skepticism and credulity,

arrogance and humility, impetuosity and conservatism, callousness and humanitarianism, and hope and disillusionment.

THE "INUTILITY" OF MEDICINE

How often did New Jersey medical men have to admit a lack of knowledge! "We record the facts"—of opposite weather conditions in Essex and Camden counties, both of which were hit by the "prevailing type" of disease at the same time—the Standing Committee of the Medical Society reported in 1864. "We admit our incompetency to explain them." Even rhetoric could not always hide this awareness of ignorance. Contagion, reported a Committee on Hospital Gangrene in 1864, is "like begetting like; the offspring of an unclean embrace that sullies the virgin purity of the blood by a detestible impregnation; a mysterious, propagable, depraved, terrible something, we know not what."

There was a good deal of self-criticism apparent in such confessions. "Pathogenic causes," the Committee continued, "are for the most part beyond our knowledge. . . . Not to appear ignorant, we talk of variations in the quantity of ozone in the atmosphere as having an influence upon health, and as being a cause of epidemical disease, and find it convenient to refer everything to these." In the same vein, the Standing Committee of the Society commented, in 1881, that "Malaria [is] a word used to cover professional indolence and ignorance."

Sometimes one can detect an undertone of pathos and futility. "I was struck," wrote Dr. Alexander Marcy of Camden, when reporting two dysentery deaths, "all through the treatment, with the utter inutility of medicine." But there was a vague awareness of knowledge yet to be gained. "The cycles [of diseases] are under influences yet to be sought out and demonstrated by future philosophic inquiry," stated the Standing Committee in 1862. Always there seemed to be, indeed there had to be, an awareness of something still unknown; but where there was awareness of shortcomings and ignorance, there was of course confusion.

THE PROBLEMS OF CAUSATION AND CONTAGION

Thus the profession argued almost incessantly the causal factors of malaria and other fevers. The old beliefs in miasmatic, telluric, and meteorological causes, for which there were many authorities all the way from Hippocrates to Hermann Boerhaave, to Noah Webster, continued to be debated, and apparently generally accepted until the end of the century. Even tetanus was said to be, in 1874, "a morbid condition of the nervous system arising from a peculiarity of local atmosphere and local geology one or both."

But contradictions were obvious. As early as the 1820's, and again in the 1860's and 1880's, it was noted that fevers were to be found where the usual miasmatic conditions from newly-turned earth, marshes, or decaying vegetable matter did not exist. Dr. Ezra Hunt, later to gain fame as a sanitarian, noted the opposite situation in 1866:

In another case of large excavations . . . . which became filled with water, and on the edges of which many Irish families [immigrants were believed to be especially susceptible] had located, I had prophesied much intermittent sickness but was disappointed to find them enjoying usual health.

In the 1880's when it was at least becoming evident that other etiological factors were involved, the theory of marsh miasma was enlarged to include "the germ and spore theory," and newly-dug earth was believed to unleash the infectious matter. Even then it was still thought necessary, as it had been in 1824, for inquiry to be made "into thermal and meteorological conditions." That this had been done for at least a century, without result—for there seemed little attempt at actual statistical correlation of meteorological events and disease in any but the vaguest way—made no difference, apparently. In any case, it probably surprised no one when the Gloucester County correspondent reported that "the miasmatic influence is at work" in 1885.

While the problem of etiology remained perplexing, the related issue of contagion could hardly be resolved. "The jousting knights of controversy," pontificated Dr. Abraham Coles in 1864, "advancing from opposite parts of the field, mingle their plumes in a contest which has reference probably to diverse aspects of the same truth. It is this way we reconcile the honest sincerities of antagonistic belief." There is little evidence that there was any reconciliation, and indeed, in the circumstances, it is doubtful that there could be. Debate, vacillation, and uncertainty on the subject were common at least through the 1870's.

Lest this seem to suggest that New Jersey physicians were either unaware of the significant demonstrations abroad of the communicability of disease, or too conservative to accept these findings, or too unimaginative to relate what had been so dramatically proven for cholera, measles, and typhoid fever, to other epidemic diseases, it needs to be pointed out that certain phenomena persisted that seemed to contradict the general acceptance of the idea of contagion. The facts that some who were exposed to the disease did not contract it, that the same disease did not attack all with equal virulency, and that some were attacked without a discernible trail of communication, continued to raise doubts. We cannot expect the physician of the time—before the general acceptance of the germ theory of disease, and before any specific knowledge of immunity, or of strain variations or life cycles among organisms—to have disregarded these doubts.

THE PROBLEM OF DISEASE IDENTIFICATION

Still another problem that beset the nineteenth-century practitioner was that of disease identification. Fevers were amorphously labeled "Intermittent," "Remittent," "Bilious," "Malarial," and combinations of these like "Bilious Remittent." In 1861 a Newark physician sought to convince his colleagues that diphtheria was a "distinct disease," distinguishable from the anginose form of scarlet fever in which there was severe throat infection. Two years later it was stated, "The profession needs a more accurate diagnosis of Diphtheria," and still a year later Dr. A. B. Dayton acknowledged previous error and accepted diphtheria as a disease *sui generis.* In 1879 the *Country Practitioner,* published in Beverly, posed to its readers the query: "Can the same poison entering a household produce in one child Diphtheria, and in another Scarlatina?" The similar inability to distinguish accurately between typhoid and malaria led to frequent references to "typho-malarial fever," although later researches were to indicate a good basis for such confusion.

No wonder that Dr. Charles Hasbrouck chose as the topic for an essay, in 1869, "The Apparent Uncertainties of Medicine, As Seen in the Conflicts and Discrepancies of Medical Opinions and Practices." Hasbrouck took refuge in the medical theory of the time in a way that served only to point up rather than to clarify the uncertainties.

HEROIC MEDICINE AND ITS DECLINE

The demigod of American medicine at the beginning of the nineteenth century was Benjamin Rush of Philadelphia. He had put forth, as was noted at the end of the last chapter, a monistic theory of disease that held that every disease was "irregular convulsive or wrong action in the system affected." This resulted, he contended, in a disturbance of the capillaries and thereby a hypertension of the whole circulatory system. The therapy —and this ushered in an age of "heroic" medicine, heroic because of the dauntlessness with which the physician went to extremes—was copious bleeding and strong purging, particularly with calomel. Venesection (bloodletting or phlebotomy), now given a further rational basis, increased in popularity and did not disappear in New Jersey until the end of the century. We shall have a brief look at its history in the State a little later.

First, though, a glance at heroic medicine. Dr. E. Michener, a New Jersey physician who practiced medicine for over fifty years, once told his colleagues that, at the Philadelphia Dispensary where he studied in 1816, the "custom was to direct [that] blood [be] taken by the ounce—10 oz., 20 oz., *etc.*" (Italics added.) The modern patient needs to be reminded that the full test tube of blood taken from his arm as he averts his eyes contains less than an ounce, and that there are 16 ounces in a pint.

Perhaps a fuller picture of heroic practices can be derived from a portion of the summation of county reports by Dr. Lewis Condict of New Brunswick in 1829:

"During the present Spring," continues Dr. Goble, "the prevalence of a cold and humid atmosphere has been particularly favorable to the production of croup; and more children have perished from that disease than at any former period. In several cases, I have found bleeding indispensably necessary. In the incipient stages I have always employed emetics, which often break the violence of the attacks. But if not, and the second . . . stage succeed, I at once resort to the lancet." Dr. Goble administers calomel, and tart. antim. combined, in small doses and at short intervals, so as to vomit and purge simultaneously. . . . It will be found, however, that in some instances of severe croup the intestinal part of the canal can scarcely be roused to act at all; and young practitioners will scarcely credit the quantities of drastic purgatives sometimes given without effect. I have frequently seen the stomach of children of two and four years retain calomel in doses of twenty to sixty grains, repeated at intervals two hours for a half a day or more, without any effect, and whilst infusion of

An illustration from the *Transactions of the Medical Society of New Jersey* for 1859. The destruction of the jaw was attributed to calomel

senna and doses of castor oil were also administered as auxiliaries. In these cases . . . I have found the elaterium to be a valuable medicine, in doses of one-quarter to one-half grain, repeated at intervals of two hours, and aided, if necessary, by tobacco injections. Gamboge may also be combined with calomel, to give it more activity. I have heard of croton oil given in such cases, but should consider it too virulent and drastic . . . for young children.

. . . I know of no remedy so competent to arrest the danger as the lancet. . . . When leeches are at hand, I should rely much on them, applied freely to the throat and neck . . . but where they cannot be had, blisters may be used to great advantage, applied to the throat and sternum. Professor Goodman has strongly recommended the use of the snuff plaster, applied to the throat. . . . Whoever has witnessed the effect of tobacco on a child, can not doubt its potency as an agent.

Dr. Condict also noted that, "An epidemic catarrh, resembling influenza . . . . generally has called for copious depletion—frequently for the lancet. . . . An old lady of eighty-nine years, under my care, was twice copiously bled . . . as was another of about sixty." The Sussex County correspondent reported that there the "Spring diseases have been pleurisy and pneumonia, highly inflammatory, but generally yielding to active depletion." Another from the same county reported "bilious remittent fever . . . requiring at first copious and repeated depletion." And so it went, depletion and deprivation, for the croup, influenza, pneumonia, and malaria, for did not Rush proclaim, "There is but one disease in the world"?

But Rush's ideas did not go uncriticized by New Jersey practitioners. About 1830 Dr. Jabez Gwinnup, addressing the Warren County Society, severely criticized the indiscriminate use of the lancet and calomel which Rush's influence had set going. Eight years earlier, Dr. William Johnson of Hunterdon County (another rural county) believed that "we err in purging too much in this disease [dysentery] and to this cause I attribute, in a great measure, the mortality attending its march." In the same year, 1822, the Standing Committee of the State Society, in a rare statement of disapproval of a correspondent's report, said, "We cannot but regret that in his zeal to promote evacuations, the doctor should have found it necessary to prescribe such extravagantly large doses. . . . we cannot but caution those less informed of the peculiarity of such disease [remittent bilious fever], from adopting such large doses of our most active medicines." The "Samson of the materia medica," as the mercurial preparation known as calomel was called in 1850, was severely criticized in 1853 by a committee of the State Society on "The Effects of Mercurial Preparation on the Living Animal Tissues." None "but the most robust can take it [mercury] into their circulation without obvious injury," the report concluded, but calomel was still holding on, although clearly losing its popularity, in the 1870's.

Theoretical considerations also played their part in the decline of heroic medicine. In 1861 Dr. Ezra M. Hunt presented a "mento-nervous" view of man—in which there are to be found some good insights into psychosomatic medicine—and called for an end to heroic medicine. His therapeutics included sedatives, stimulants, and tonics. Instead of bleeding, opium was to be used; instead of the lancet, emetics, or cathartics, the new concept called for veratrum, belladonna, aconite, strychnine, and hydrocyanic acid. Poisonous, yes, but only *multum in parvo* heroics.

Similarly, before the decade was over, Dr. Charles Hasbrouck reached like conclusions by a different theoretical route. Resorting largely to Brunonian theory, Hasbrouck thought of disease as either "sthenic" (exciting) and requiring sedatives, tonics, and narcotics; or "asthenic" (debilitating) and requiring a different kind of sedative, tonics, and stimulants. His therapeutics included such sedatives as venesection, evacuants, *Veratrum viride,* aconite, and antimony. His narcotic was opium and his stimulants were ammonia and brandy.

Both Hunt and Hasbrouck were advocating a more

moderate approach to therapeutics. This was perhaps a consequence of what seems to have been a changing pattern of disease in New Jersey in the 1850's and 1860's. "The diseases have been more asthenic than usual," stated one report in 1850, "few requiring blood-letting or free depletion by purgatives." This change from the sthenic to asthenic character of sickness led another physician to comment in 1863, "Our lancets rust in their cases, and our former heroic remedies remain neglected on our shelves."

But other factors were also at work moderating the therapeutics of mid-century. Certainly the impact of the yet-unorthodox Thomsonian school and its botanical theory that rejected mineral drugs was not without effect. Even the homeopaths, whose ideas will be discussed later, were grudgingly credited with pointing up the tendency of diseases to cure themselves without heroic therapy. More important, perhaps, was the influence of the therapeutic nihilism that had spread out of the school of pathologic anatomy at Vienna. This school taught that disease was a local rather than a constitutional manifestation—humoral pathology of the ancients and monistic theoretical pathology of the eighteenth and nineteenth century to the contrary notwithstanding. Medicines, since their effect was constitutional, availed little. Dr. Hasbrouck, former Brunonian, in a rather grudging recognition of the new pathology, had to agree that derangements of "vital actions" resulted in "morbid changes in the structure and functions of the organism." Moreover, he concluded, "We know that derangements and changes are usually self-limited, and for the most part remediable by the natural recuperative powers, provided we can place our patients in harmony with natural hygienic conditions." Thirteen years later, Dr. George T. Welch of Keyport pointed out that the young doctor believed in the magic of drugs, the old doctor looked "upon the most of them as mischievous," while the "pathologist is skeptical of them all." Medicines were administered, he went on, "as if disease lay in its phenomena and not in the organic conditions out of which they spring." From Milton he borrowed the line, "They also serve who only stand and wait." At most, he advocated treatment by tonics and stimulants and, reminiscent of Oliver Wendell Holmes, he went on to assert that, "if certain drugs, like opium, iodine, phosphorous, iron, ether, strychnia, and aconite were rescued, the whole nauseous bulk of the rest might be in the flat seas sunk, and the death-rate rise no higher."

But the decline in heroic medicine was based, more than on any of the foregoing reasons, on pragmatic considerations. "A number of physicians were invited to see this case," ran a report in 1863, "whose suggestions were eagerly listened to, and . . . acted upon. Having exhausted our armamentarium, the case was abandoned to nature; a general improvement took place, and the girl is now comparatively well." More important was the opinion that seemed to be forming that to "follow out the practice of blood-letting and purgation, is in many cases to consign the patient to an untimely grave."

Dr. R. H. Page of Burlington County used the pages of the *Country Practitioner* to declaim against a broader spectrum of drugs and dosages: "veratrum viridi has filled many a grave; hydrate of chloral hushed many a victim; chloroform a holocaust of death, and the thousand and one recommendations that appear of knock-down, drag-out doses of powerful drugs . . . have produced much evil." And in a later, pointed comment on the quality of the medicine practiced in New Jersey, as demonstrated by the communications from the county correspondents, Dr. Welch bitingly called attention to "The most unconquerable diseases [that] have been cured by the most unreasonable medicines . . . . most of [which] are poisons."

Even as the heroics were giving way to more moderate therapeutics, "the unloading of the capillaries by sedation, depletion, and de[p]rivation" was still being advised. "The whole art of medicine" it was still believed by some, consisted "of knowing when to stimulate and when to deplete." But there was a difference—calomel and opium were being replaced by quinine and iron, "because they have fewer pathogenic effects."

VENESECTION

Blood-letting as a basic procedure in heroic therapeutics came under the same attack from both pathologic anatomists and the practicing physicians. In France its value had been subjected to statistical examination as early as 1835 by Pierre Louis. The vicissitudes of the practice in New Jersey are worth special attention.

For a time, early in the century, on the authority of the Standing Committee of the State Society, venesection apparently had fallen into disfavor. By 1824, however, the Committee could report that it (venesection) had "within a few years acquired an increased practice and reputation," especially in the eastern part of the State. Thereafter it continued in general use, in the 1850's in fevers generally, and although it fell into some disfavor later because of the purported change in the nature of fevers from sthenic to asthenic, it continued in use in the early stages of sthenic diseases. Its one-time use in puerperal convulsions was revived in 1860, and its use in such conditions appears in the records for at least twenty years thereafter. In 1873 it was reported from rural Cumberland County, "Venesection is seldom practiced in this district," but in 1875 the "lost art"—to use the contemporary allusion—was "again coming into favor" in the State. In 1885 it was again said to be "gaining ground" in Gloucester County, but the next year it was reported that "few of the present members of the Camden County Medical Society have ever bled a patient."

In 1881, when Dr. E. Michener looked back at his half-century of practice, he criticized the profession for abandoning the conflict with disease, "leaving it to pursue its destructive course. . . . For more than half a century I used the lancet very freely . . . and to an extent which few physicians seem willing to imitate. But now . . . the retrospect of the past brings up vastly more regrets for the *omission* than for the *employment* of the remedy." Dr. Michener's words brought forth the applause of the noted Dr. S. D. Gross in Philadelphia. "In the Jefferson Medical College," he wrote to the *Country Practitioner* which had carried Dr. Michener's comments, "I dwell with much force and emphasis upon the employment of the lancet in early stages of inflammatory affections. . . . I wish to God that it were in my power to write the sentence in letters of fire upon the brain of every practicing physician and surgeon in the civilized world." Dr. Gross had delivered a lengthy discourse on blood-letting to the American Medical Association in 1875; the New Jersey *Country Practitioner* reprinted it in 1881. Obviously, Oliver Wendell Holmes had been figuratively too sanguine and literally not sanguine enough when he had stated in 1861 that venesection had gone out of fashion in the United States and in Great Britain.

THE GERM THEORY OF DISEASE

There was thus, it is now evident, something of a state of confusion in medicine when the germ theory of disease first began to make an impression on New Jersey medicine. Etiology and whether disease was a local or constitutional manifestation were matters of contention. Disease entities were not readily identifiable and differentiated. Therapeutics, reflecting this confused state of affairs, often reverted to a simple practicalism as its escape from doubt.

Modern interest in the germ theory of disease—with germs interpreted as living organisms of some kind—starts with the work of Christian C. Ehrenberg. His atlas of the *Infusionsthierchen* appeared in 1838, and created a great deal of interest in the animalculum as a cause of disease. In the United States in the late 1840's and 1850's there were those who were claiming animalcular origins of transmission for cholera, yellow fever, and other diseases. The convincing demonstration of the pathogenic role of organisms occurred in the late 1870's with the work of Louis Pasteur and Robert Koch.

There seems to be one association of New Jersey with the early discussion of animalcula. It appeared, not in a medical work, but in a dental work by the Jerseyman Samuel C. Harbert. His excellent *A Practical Treatise on the Operations of Surgical and Mechanical Dentistry* was published in Philadelphia in 1847. Harbert noted that Leuwenhoek had said that the human mouth was populated by infusory animals, and Harbert cited recent microscopic studies of dental tartar in Paris that indicated that the "human mouth was a perfect cemetery, where millions of infusoria find their catacombs." This Harbert questioned, indicating that he believed that the infusoria were spontaneously generated in the interval between the mouth and the microscope.

Not until the 1870's does there seem to have been any appreciable interest in the germ theory of disease among New Jersey medical men. When it was introduced, it added to the prevailing confusion. Take, for example, the statement in 1871 of Dr. J. E. Culver of Hudson City:

I confess to have lost faith in "marsh miasmata" and, indeed in all ideal creations assigned as intangible substitutes for etiological knowledge. The authors and worshippers of unknown gods, reckless of the pedigrees of ills to be engendered, have turned loose such a motley multitude of "specific poisons" and "animalculae," and "vegetations," and "germs," and "spores," into the atmosphere—not to mention our food and drink—that the wonder is that mankind are not all continually sick, with promiscuous generations of hybrid diseases, of ever-varying types, baffling nosology and setting at naught the established rules of therapeutics.

Two years later another commentator answered one of the questions in Culver's mind. "All infectious diseases . . . are disseminated throughout the land, attached to materials of every kind . . . awaiting for a time . . . for the person . . . who affords no resistance or has an affinity for such sporules." Here we have a rudimentary notion of immunity, and a recognition that the organism by itself is not the complete etiological story. The differentiation in the early nineteenth century between approximate and exciting causes seemed more appropriate now than ever, and the dependence of a local infection on general constitutional health—or tone, to use the older concept—might have given reassurance that the debates between the localists and constitutionalists were not mere vanities.

Despite some uncertainty as to the nature of the organisms that caused disease—bacteria were defined by Dr. R. H. Page in 1879 as "microscopic animalcular ferments or poisons"—and a lack of clear distinctions between germs, spores, and parasitic life, the general theory gained increasing acceptance. In 1876 several facets of Pasteur's work were reported to the Medical Society of New Jersey and, cautiously presenting the arguments in favor of the germ theory of disease, the speaker pointed out, with neither conviction nor conclusiveness, that the presence of the same organisms in each case of the same disease suggested that they bore a causative relation to that disease. In 1880, Dr. D. Benjamin of Camden presented a good history of the germ theory of disease for the readers of the *Country Practitioner,* and in 1885 President O. C. Barber, of the State Society, pointed out the epochal significance of the theory, although he did not seem quite certain that it would stand the test of time. Barber's paper also presented an interesting historical account of the development of the theory, but went on to a lengthy discussion of the "methods of cultivation" of micro-organisms. The inclusion of the last points out that the profession was yet unfamiliar with the new bacteriological techniques, and, indeed, bacteriology was not yet a subject among those recommended by the American Medical Association for examination by state boards.

Barber went on to list ten diseases for which bacteria had been reported, pointed to the theory that the toxic action of germs derived from their excretory products, and stated that many micro-organisms were not pathogenic and were apparently destroyed by the leucocytes. The severity of an epidemic might depend upon the source from which the organisms were derived, and the condition of their development. Altogether, a great deal of information and a great deal of educated guessing were passed on to "the busy and hard working practitioner who . . . has little time for reading," so that he could be " 'au courant' with the times upon this subject."

Barber stopped short in his presentation. He said nothing about diagnosis or therapeutics. Indeed there was little to be said on either subject: diagnostic clinics were not yet available and few doctors were capable of microscopic analysis. A Dr. Stickler of Orange had reported the year before that he had found foreign matter in the water tank of the house in which there were sick children. Under the microscope he discovered "very small bodies, round and staff-shaped, which were very active." But he was "not prepared to say that these small bodies were the agents which gave rise to the sickness." Significant changes in therapeutics would have to await new developments in immunology and chemotherapy.

There were, however, those who would not accept the germ theory of disease, or at least did not do so at once. Why did people recover, why did certain individuals escape, why did diseases attack with different violence, they asked. The validity of the germ theory continued to be debated in the early 1880's; indeed so much discussion took place that, as one exaggeration had it, in 1881, "it is now almost hazardous to speak of germs in a medical assembly. . . . At present germs, cells, sporules, bacteria, micrococci, *et genus omni* are meeting with some opposition, and are obliged to establish their reputation for mischief more fully." Obviously the germ theory did not and could not at once dispel and replace the accumulations of centuries of theory and practice.

III

DISEASE AND THERAPEUTICS IN
THE NINETEENTH CENTURY

Disease seems never to be absent, and the doctor's work seems never to be done. One could select at random from among the reports of the county correspondents to the Standing Committee of the State Society and quickly be impressed with the pervasiveness of disease and the industriousness of the practitioner in the nineteenth century. For example, there was the report of Dr. William Johnson from Hunterdon County:

He remarks that the Winter of 1822 was not very sickly; the diseases of the first three months were synochus, though sometimes typhus. . . . [They] generally came to a crisis within a fortnight; very little mortality attended it. . . .

Late in March the hooping cough appeared. . . . Some cases of dysentery occurred in May, its attacks were renewed the last of July, and continued during the months of August, September, and October; it prevailed extensively. . . . The mortality appears to have been great, especially among very young subjects. . . .

Tertian fevers were rife Summer and Autumn. . . .

At the close of Summer a bilious and typhoid fever occurred, and at the end of the year, pneumonia and rheumatism.

Little wonder that Dr. John R. Stevenson, writing of

his practice in the 1860's, remarked, "The daily routine of a physician's visits to his sick patients gives but a faint idea of the vast amount of disease and infirmity that exist throughout the land. The number of men among us who are feeble, deformed, or diseased, is very great indeed— far beyond the belief of anyone who has not seen them with his own eyes." He reported that between November 23, 1863, and January 5, 1864, 333 draftees were found medically unfit for duty out of 675 examined in the then First Congressional District of New Jersey in south Jersey. They suffered from some sixty conditions, ranging from stammering to imbecility to Bright's disease. Hernia was the chief culprit, accounting for more eliminations than fractures, dislocations, and hand injuries together. Phthisis (tuberculosis), asthma, and heart disease were also significant.

It would indeed be a virtually impossible task to recount the year-by-year epidemic and endemic diseases in nineteenth-century New Jersey. Yellow fever seemed scarcely to be mentioned, and even Camden seems to have escaped the several attacks of the disease in Philadelphia. Malaria was reported to have "ceased to exist" in the State by the Standing Committee of the State Society in 1860, but this is hardly in agreement with the morbidity and mortality statistics in either Camden or Newark at the time.

In the 1870's there was said to be current the "impression, in neighboring and especially eastern states, that for one to live in Newark is to become a victim of chills and fever." Camden was visited by an epidemic in 1877. By 1880 the Standing Committee was ready to acknowledge that the disease was almost universally present in the State, and in 1882 it was reported to be resuming its "former prestige." It seemed to almost disappear in the 1890's, for reasons still something of a puzzle, for all the necessary conditions were still to be found. Typhoid fever, still confused with malaria, ravaged right along with it and indeed outlasted it. Despite all the advances in sanitation, it was difficult to get ahead of the disease.

In 1882 it prevailed in 11 of the 16 counties, and in 1891 there were 609 cases of typhoid in Newark alone. (These and subsequent statistics must be considered illustrative rather than definitive, since they reflect the confusion in diagnosis that existed.)

Scarlet fever seemed always to be present and accounted for 329 deaths in Newark in a period of sixteen months during 1859-1860, when its population was about sixty-five thousand. In 1872, 10 out of the 15 counties in the State reported this disease, and the town of Lambertville alone accounted for 300 cases. The disease was to outlive the century. The old scourge of smallpox, against which vaccination had proved effective from the start of the nineteenth century, reasserted itself as people became careless about vaccination and re-vaccination. It reappeared widely at least as early as the 1840's and continued to spread death and disfigurement, reaching epidemic proportions at least once in each decade. Again, 1872 was a bad year; smallpox was to be found in eleven counties. Traced to Philadelphia, it particularly ravaged Camden, where there were a thousand cases—in a population of about twenty-three thousand—and where it became necessary to open a special smallpox hospital. There were 157 deaths from smallpox in Camden that year. Newark in the year 1871-1872 had 930 cases and 120 fatalities, and the disease did not abate until 1874. Vaccination campaigns put on by the cities had some effect, and, although compulsory vaccination of all school children in Trenton and in Newark was a consequence of another outbreak in 1892, all school boards could not require vaccination until 1902.

Cholera was reported in New Jersey in 1832, again in the late forties, and at least three times in the fifties. Its attack in 1855 mocked the boast of the President of the State Society about the decrease in mortality and the increase in the length of human life that resulted from "the improvement in medical science and the diffusion of medical knowledge." Cholera, however, does not figure as such in the mortality statistics of the last two decades of the century.

But the real scourges of the late nineteenth century were not the old fevers and agues. They were tuberculosis, pneumonia, influenza, diarrheal diseases of children, and diphtheria. Other diseases also exacted large tolls: diseases of the central nervous system, cardiovascular diseases, typhus, mumps, measles, meningitis, whooping cough, venereal diseases, and "rheumatism."

Tuberculosis seems to have been regularly and ubiquitously present. The mortality statistics for Newark from 1859 to 1878 show it to have been by far the largest single cause of death for every year in the period. The actual number of deaths was large: 232 in 1859, a high of 505 in 1874, and 448 in 1878. The same was true for Essex County and indeed for the whole State. The mortality statistics for the State for the twenty years from 1879 to 1898 indicate that an average of 3310 died each year in New Jersey from "consumption." The great white plague began to abate a bit at the end of the century, as we shall see, but the great assault against it was to come in the twentieth century.

But the most horrible scourge of them all was diphtheria. There was something about this sickness more detestable and insidious than any of the others: its devious way of spreading, its unpleasant manifestations, its slaughter of mothers and children, its danger to doctors and nurses, and its invincibility. For it remedies needed to be desperate indeed, although there was a great deal of disagreement as to what they should be. There also continued to be considerable confusion between diphtheria and scarlet fever, although clinical distinction between the two was made in France in 1826, and the question of contagion and local versus constitutional disease with regard to diphtheria still perplexed the profession. In Newark the mortality rate for it reached 43 per 1000 deaths in 1873, in 1875 it was 111, and in 1876 it was 108. The strangling of children went on, and strong

A Remedy for Diphtheria

Make two small bags that will
reach from ear to ear and fill them with
ashes and salt dip them in hot water
and wring out so they will not drip and
apply them to the throate cover up whole with
a flannel cloth and change them as often
as they become cool untill the throate
becomes irritated near blistering for children it
is necessary to put flannel cloth between the

ashes and the throat to prevent blistering when
the ashes have been on a sufficient time take a
wet flannel cloth and rub it with Castil soap un
till it is Covered with a thick lather dip it in
hot water and apply it to the throat change
as they cool it the time use a gargle made of
one teaspoonful of Cayanne pepper one of salt
one of molassus in a teacupful of hot water and
when Coll add one fourth as much Cider vinegar
and gargle every fifteen minutes untill the
the patient requires slep gargle made of Castil
soap is good to used part of the time

The domestic treatment of diphtheria in the nineteenth century
*From the commonplace book of the Hankinson family of
Reading in the Rutgers University Library*

emetics, powerful swabs and gargles, dangerous internal medicines, unsavory counterirritants applied to the throat, and last-ditch surgical procedures availed little. Not until diphtheria antitoxin was put on the market in 1892—its use in New Jersey is recorded in 1895—did the slaughter of the innocents begin to diminish.

The Practical Approach to Medicine

How could the practitioner approach the ravages of disease, especially in the face of the uncertainty and confusion of both medical theory and practice? What could the practitioner do when he read (in 1861) that some doctors repudiated all treatment for scarlet fever, others merely prescribed palliatives, and still others continued "active treatment." Or what was he to think when, on the one hand, he was advised to use chlorate of potassium for diphtheria "freely and frequently," but, on the other, warned of its toxic qualities? What could he think when silver nitrate was regularly recommended for diphtheria in one year (1862) and called "a doubtful remedy" the next? What was he to do when suddenly he was admonished that the customary practice of throat-swabbing in diphtheria was "useless . . . improper, and reprehensible," and what should be his enlightened approach to this disease when he read that he should give "at first a Mercurial Cathartic" if the fever is high, and seven pages later, in the same journal, "no Calomel, no Purgatives." This was, after all, an age when spider web, in the form of pills, was still being prescribed for malaria even though quinine had already replaced the bark.

The answer lay in part in courage: the physician must be "brave enough [to make immediate decisions and] to assume any responsibility that the exigencies of the case may require." But mainly the answer lay in empiricism, in the practical rather than the philosophical sense of the term. "*Theorize* at home, and be prepared to *practise* at the bed-side," admonished the editor of the

Country Practitioner in 1879. "Do we know why we administered, and what we are battling?" asked Dr. James B. Coleman in 1853. "The chemist, the microscopist, and the physiologist, must determine, and if from them we do not obtain the information we seek, practice must be empirical," he continued. And empirical it seemed to be.

"Recipe doctors" carried saddlebags, "always pregnant with a promiscuous collection of remedies, concisely labeled, '*Good for Rheumatism,*' '*Good for the Piles,*' '*Good for Fever and Ague.*'" Dr. John C. Budd (1762-1845) had two favorite prescriptions: one he called "Tincture Botanae," which he gave when he did "not know what else to do, for it is *emmenagogue, sedative, cathartic, tonic, and expectorant, and cannot fail to hit somewhere.*" The other, for which, unfortunately, we have no explanation, he called "Diabolical Pills."

Therapeutics was "not an exact science," it was argued in 1868, and must depend on the doctor's judgment and experience. This meant treating symptoms: "We have to follow the indications of each particular case, and soothe, disinfect, or sustain, as symptoms seem to require," ran one typical comment in 1864. Where the remedy selected did not perform as hoped for, the practitioner ran the gamut: a tetanus patient was treated by one physician in 1874 with opium, morphine sulfate, ipecac, potassium nitrate, terebinth, tincture of asafoetida, chloral hydrate, Dover's powder, and morphine, in something of a series.

THERAPEUTICS

In the nineteenth century, heroic practices were replaced by moderation, but deprivation and depletion continued, as did the use of blisters, cupping, and leeches, and tobacco injections. Occasionally credulity and folk-medicine attained the prestige of professional approbation, as did the herb skull cap (*Scutellaria lateriflora*) as an antidote for hydrophobia, early in the century. A family secret, it was revealed first in the *Medical Repository,* and Dr. Lawrence Vandeveer of Somerset, one of the founders of the State Medical Society, declared that he had saved over three hundred (sometimes stated as four hundred) people from madness with the remedy and never lost a patient. Fifteen cases of persons bitten who escaped death when treated with excision and skull cap were reported to the Essex County Medical Society in 1823. More generally, salt pork was apparently accepted as a counterirritant to be placed around the throat of diphtheria patients. Early in the century, Dr. Jabez Gwinnup recommended a mashed ladybug to be rubbed on the gum for toothache, and Dr. D. A. Currie reported in 1863 that he had learned to use hot lard in facial erysipelas. When, however, two American medical journals carried a prescription for pneumonia which the correspondent claimed he had successfully used in each of 112 cases and would "positively cure any uncomplicated case of pneumonia in any stage from twenty-four to forty-eight hours," the New Jersey *Country Practitioner* remarked that it was no wonder that "American medical journalism is sneered at."

Specific remedies continued to be sought, however, and the nineteenth century is replete with new or revived drugs to which some special, if not specific, value was attached. As each was introduced into New Jersey, one senses the enthusiasm and hope with which it was taken up, the professional strains as critics rose to challenge claims made too optimistically, and the disillusionment that followed when sober experience indicated that much had been left to be desired. Chloroform, it was reported in 1868, taken internally in brandy, was an antispasmodic and capable of dissolving gallstones. Chloral hydrate, introduced in Germany in 1869, was widely, perhaps "indiscriminately" used in New Jersey the next year as a painkiller and hypnotic. By 1874 its anodyne and sedative actions were being questioned in Gloucester County, and although its "general utility" and "hypnotic" action were still approved there—and the drug is still of value today—the consensus elsewhere seemed to be that it was not a reliable or pleasant remedy. Salicylic acid, another chemical remedy introduced from Germany about 1875 (and sold here at $2.50 an ounce), had a most phenomenal reception, not as a specific, but rather as something of a panacea. It was first introduced in New Jersey as a gargle or spray for diphtheria, and as a "powerfully antiseptic" surgical dressing. Initially a disappointment, it continued in use nevertheless. In 1879 it was thought by some to be a specific in rheumatic fever, and in 1880 it was recommended for diabetes. Carbolic acid became even more of a fad. Dr. C. F. J. Lehlbach of Newark, who made pious obeisance to the need for understanding the physiological mode of action of medicines, nevertheless recommended carbolic acid for no less than 15 conditions, most of them dermatological, but also including gonorrhea, by injection; chancre; diphtheria, as a gargle and penciling solution; and, internally, for diarrhea in children in small, virtually homeopathic, doses; and for sickness of pregnancy. Beset by the limitations of medicine, the physician was perhaps ready to seize upon anything of promise; his willingness and need to test drugs in the crucible of the human body, however, would have been less subject to criticism had he paid more attention to the new physiological and pharmacological sciences.

One of the most common remedies in use in the nineteenth century was *Veratrum viride,* otherwise known as pokeroot, or swamp hellebore. Found in the *London Pharmacopoeia* of 1746, this dangerous drug was omitted in later issues. Cullen had gone so far as to say it was "a very poisonous plant, which I would hardly think of employing even upon the authority of the estimable Conrad Gesner," and its very violent action was recognized by American authorities. But an English physician had reported using it effectively in gout, and the American Dr. Wesley C. Norwood introduced a tincture of it whose success in reducing the pulse was "well established by its trial in the New York Emigrant [*sic*] Hospital." Thereafter it was often used in New Jersey in a variety of diseases, from diphtheria to pneumonia, as a kind of sedative in place of blood-letting. The report in 1879 that "few use it now" was probably premature.

Finally, mention must be made of ergot, which, though other uses were found for it, became so commonly used in childbirth as to appear to revolutionize obstetrical procedures. But a second look advised caution. In 1856 Dr. William Pierson pointed out the dangers, and as a consequence, when Dr. Charles Hasbrouck examined his own practice he discovered that there were ten stillbirths out of twenty-seven cases where ergot had been used, while there were only three out of nineteen cases where he had used the forceps.

This hardly exhausts the remedies introduced and used in New Jersey. Many more were in use, and aconite, jaborandi, potassium chlorate, and silver nitrate are perhaps worthy of special mention. As the century progressed, the chemical industry became increasingly active in the manufacture of pharmaceuticals, and bromides, iodides, hypophosphites, and ferric phosphates joined the vast materia medica.

The main stand-bys, however, remained the opiates and quinine. The latter rapidly replaced the bark after the work of Pelletier and Caventou in France. As early as 1829 sulphate of quinine was in use in New Jersey, and thereafter virtually every fever—certainly if it showed any cyclical tendencies—called for the use of quinine. Opium, morphine, and morphine sulfate were constantly and rather freely in use for almost any sort of pain or discomfort. In 1877 Dr. Elias J. Marsh of Newark had no compunction about reporting the use of morphine on himself for hay fever relief.

The most common mode of administering morphine at this time was the hypodermic needle. Introduced by an Irish physician in 1844, the hypodermic seemed to have come into general use in New Jersey in the 1860's. Dr. Samuel C. Thornton was using it quite regularly in 1869, even going to the extent of first chloroforming a patient who dreaded the instrument. He called his colleagues' attention to the aphorism, "A country doctor should never start on his rounds without a syringe and a bottle of morphia solution." City doctor, G. R. Kent, of Newark reported in 1874 that "I could scarcely get along without my hypodermic syringe." He used injections of morphia in cholera morbis, colic, acute rheumatism, various forms of inflammatory diseases, and neuralgia "with marked benefit."

In 1874 the Standing Committee of the State Society noted that the hypodermic needle was extensively employed in medical practice and called it a safe remedial procedure. Morphia was the drug most frequently used. In the same year Dr. J. W. Pinkham of Montclair reported that he had used the instrument for seven years, and "upwards of three thousand times." Dr. Edgar Holden of Newark reported having given injections to one patient for 45 consecutive days, and that he had given from fifty to sixty injections to a single patient during the course of a disease: "hepatic colic, hereditary." Dr. J. W. Pinkham, who had begun to use the hypodermic needle in 1867, reported seven years later that he had administered injections "with constantly increasing favor" not only of morphia, but also of atropia, strychnia, hydrate of chloral, ergot, and quinia. Other drugs were also introduced by the needle, and the practice became so general that pharmaceutical houses were putting out kits of vials of soluble tablets of various drugs for hypodermic application, one such kit containing, at the turn of the century, no fewer than 146 varieties.

By 1874, danger signs were evident. One doctor admitted that the "importunities" of a woman patient "for the use of the syringe" were "so urgent, as to make him regret the invention of the instrument." The growing problem of narcotic addiction became of particular concern to the physician because of his awareness of his own culpability. Dr. J. B. Mattison, in a paper on "Opium Inebriety," pointed the way for the doctor in 1878. He called for diminished prescribing, careful screening of patients, intermittent administration at increasing intervals, and pre-emptory abandonment when no longer needed. Moreover, Mattison called for "legislative interference" that would prohibit both the dispensing of such drugs without a prescription and the refilling of prescriptions, desiderata that were to take forty-six years to obtain.

IV

MEDICAL SCIENCE AND PROGRESS
IN THE NINETEENTH CENTURY

T HUS FAR it would appear that medicine in New Jersey
was in a rather parlous state. Little has as yet been said
to indicate any appreciable development in scientific
medicine or interest in research. Here again New Jersey
was not different from other places. Medical historian
Richard H. Shryock has pointed out that medical research was a concomitant of an urban culture, but New
Jersey, though urbanization proceeded apace, was to be
overshadowed by the metropolises on either side of her.
Indeed a lack of originality in research marked not only
New Jersey medicine, but even the great centers of academic medicine in the United States before 1895.

In New Jersey, where the practitioner was concerned
with current problems and not with long-run improvement, there is evidence of an awareness of such shortcomings. "No act has been committed or enterprise
commenced, to promote science, which gives her [the
Medical Society] a conspicuous character among her con-
temporaries, or will enroll her name on the page of
history," lamented the Standing Committee in 1828.
Forty years later, having in the meantime made several
ineffective attempts at promoting research and scientific
interests, the State Society disclaimed any responsibility
for "leadership in purely scientific medical progress." It
saw its role as professional and ethical, and was willing to

leave science to "the labors of smaller bodies." "As physicians, neither the past nor present generation of practitioners in Burlington County," stated the report from that County in 1866, "have aimed at scientific prominence. Isolated as we are, we have not the advantage of that attrition, which in compact communities burnishes the crude mineral into the polished gem, but sound practical good sense has at all times been characteristic of our physicians." Perhaps this was just as well, for, as Comte had said, to have left research to the practitioners would have been as unfortunate as if astronomy had been turned over to ship captains. "I have no time tonight to examine authorities" is the revealing way in which Dr. A. B. Dayton of Middletown bluntly brought his communication to the Standing Committee to an end in 1862.

Yet medical men in New Jersey were aware of the advances in science and medicine, and they were exhibiting scientific interests and insights that reflected the best in medical science. In the face of what has been said of the empirical nature of medical practice in New Jersey, it may seem something of an anomaly to speak now of scientific medicine in New Jersey in the nineteenth century. But the facts are that the older practitioner was kept informed of innovations, no matter how overwhelmed he may have been by them, and the younger practitioner was increasingly the product of a more scientific training.

Physical Diagnosis

The introduction of new techniques of physical diagnosis was one of the significant advances of medicine in the last century. Two very basic such techniques were percussion (detecting internal conditions from the resonance resulting from striking the surface) and auscultation (listening to internal sounds). The former was introduced by Leopold Auenbrugger of Vienna in 1761 and the use of the stethoscope in the latter was introduced by René Laennec in 1819, but neither procedure took hold anywhere very rapidly. Not until 1852 do we find any significant mention of them in New Jersey literature. In that year the President of the Medical Society of New Jersey noted that these procedures had been taught with great certainty and success, and thereafter such references as those to the stethoscope and the chest sounds called "rales" (1860), percussion and "vesicular murmur" (1863), and auscultation and "clearer rules" of determining pneumonia (1868) are common enough in the New Jersey accounts.

Pulse-taking also became more exact and meaningful. At least as early as 1856, and frequently thereafter, precise pulse-counts were noted. The character of the pulse also took on significance.

The thermometer, though it was first introduced into clinical practice in France in the eighteenth century, did not come into general hospital use in England until the 1860's, and the first elaborate account of its use did not appear in Europe until 1868. In New Jersey it was said to be introduced as a measure of the "intensity of disease" in 1870. It was not, however, immediately popular; in 1877 it was stated that although it was becoming as important as the stethoscope, those without hospital training "find some difficulty [in] its thorough appreciation."

Acquaintance with other instruments of physical diagnosis, if not their actual use, seems also to have been made in New Jersey in the 1870's. It would indeed be a formidable task to make a complete list of the various species and subspecies of scope, meter, and graph that are mentioned in the two decades of the seventies and eighties. Some have become common enough—the laryngoscope (the subject of a paper before the Mercer County Medical Society in 1868), the ophthalmoscope, the otoscope, for example. Others suggest that perhaps some were overextending the new science, the "dynamometer," for example, which measured "decreased muscular contraction and inferrentially defective innervation." However, most of the new instruments were either unknown or not used by the general practitioner. When Cornelius Larison, country doctor, died in 1910 after forty-five years of practice, his medical equipment included no diagnostic instrument except the stethoscope. A forceps; other obstetrical, surgical and tooth-pulling instruments; splints and bandages; a mortar and pestle; and a set of balances completed the inventory.

With one of these instruments, the name of a New Jersey physician is closely linked. The sphygmograph, which measured and traced on paper the arterial pulse and which was to become an important aid in the diagnosis of heart disease, had been developed by Vierordt in Germany in 1855 and Marey in France in 1860. Dr. Edgar Holden of Newark, having had difficulty in operating Marey's apparatus for three years, devised an instrument which he first presented in the *Medical Record,* and later, with illustrations of the graphs he obtained, in the *Transactions* of the New Jersey Society (1871). Although others had also made improvements on the instrument in the meantime, Dr. Holden was credited thirteen years later—by a New Jersey colleague to be sure—with having developed "the most perfect instrument."

Finally, before the end of the century, the X ray was already in use in New Jersey. A report of an operation for the removal of a foreign body in the esophagus in 1898 given to the State Society included a "Skiograph" by which the object was located, and which was reproduced in the *Transactions.*

This account of the diagnostic devices should not be taken to mean that other diagnostic procedures of varying degrees of objectivity were unknown to the New Jersey practitioner. He knew, for example, of the use of a chemical reagent (nitric acid) in testing urine for albumin (1863); he measured the specific gravity of urine in diagnosing diabetes insipidus (1875); he used the sound in examining for the stone (1860); and he made use of the vaginal speculum (1872). The dates here are to be considered illustrative rather than primary.

THE SCIENCE OF MEDICINE

New Jersey medicine was also kept abreast of developments and ideas in pharmacology and physiology. The danger that mercury would arrest the process of tissue oxygenation and destroy the "albuminous principles of the blood," the justification of the use of quinine in malaria only, the danger in carrying the use of ergot too far, for example, were pointed out in 1868. The endocrine basis of disease was reported in 1878 by Dr. Alexander N. Dougherty, who had studied in Paris in the mid-fifties. Glycosuria (which he considered a broad term that included diabetes mellitus) he described as belonging to a "class" of disease "characterized by chemical abnormalities in the secretions or fluids of the body." To him the doctrine was becoming prevalent that disease was not an entity, but a "want of physiological equilibrium" —something of a nineteenth-century verification of humoral pathology.

The interest in gross pathology (i.e., of an entire organ) is evident throughout the century. In 1838 the State Society sought legislation facilitating dissection—a law attained for a few years in 1895 and then not again until 1907. About 1847 the complete membrane from the throat of a child who had died of croup was exhibited before the Burlington County Society. In 1867 the country physician was exhorted to make more frequent post-mortem examinations "for the correction of diagnosis, and justification, or not, of the practice pursued." In 1870 there was in existence a Hudson County Pathological Society, and in 1879 the Report of the Essex County Hospital for the Insane mentioned the performance of 22 post-mortems.

As the influence of the German school of pathology

spread, more attention was paid to the microscopic examination of tissue. In 1860 there is a report of brain tissue being sent to New York from Orange for microscopic analysis, and in 1863 there is a microscopic report that specified a "medullary osteosarcoma." Although other such instances are readily found, the use of the microscope proceeded slowly: the instrument is not mentioned in the catalogue of the Harvard Medical School until 1870 and there was no opportunity for students to learn microscopy at the Columbia College of Physicians and Surgeons in 1872. The existence of a New Brunswick Microscopical Society in 1868 and another in Camden in 1879 (or earlier) is therefore not a very belated interest in micoscopy. In 1875 Dr. G. C. Freeborn was appointed microscopist at St. Michael Hospital in Newark, an indication of new things to come.

The medical potential of the microscope was well demonstrated in a paper in 1875 by Dr. A. M. Edwards of Newark on the use of the microscope in gynecology. Dr. Edwards was struggling with the problems of preserving specimens of vaginal discharges for microscopic exhibition, but even more important he reported finding, and illustrated with drawings, the *trichomonas vaginalis*. Moreover, he described the organism subdividing longitudinally into two new ones, a phenomenon which he claimed "has never been hitherto described."

Edwards' paper is one of a good many that demonstrate the coming of age of New Jersey medicine. Another was Dr. Dougherty's paper on "Glycosuria" already mentioned. This was a careful and valuable résumé of the knowledge of diabetes in 1878; he included the work of a Lancereaux on the pancreas and described the pathology of the disease and Fehling's test for sugar in the urine. His treatment was mainly dietetic, and he recommended especially "Camplin biscuits" made of flour from starchless bran and named after their English inventor. He concluded with an array of cases.

As the century went on, it was becoming more and more evident that there were men of scientific bent in

New Jersey, men with the intellectual acumen and a strong enough sense of mission to overcome the handicaps of the constant and immediate pressure of practice. The results of some of their work are startling in their modernity. There was, for example, the paper on hay fever and asthma presented by Dr. E. J. Marsh in 1877. Dr. Marsh went through an excellent historical account of the diseases, and knew of ragweed, pollen, and such. The personal "idiosyncrasies" he spoke of could readily be translated into "allergies" today. Dr. W. Nichols' talk on "Old Age" in 1850 was an intelligent study of the processes of aging and the care of the aged, long before the term "geriatrics" came into general use. There is something most up-to-date in Dr. Joseph Parrish's demand that alcoholism be removed from the domain of morals and be dealt with as a neurotic disorder. He contended that it was a disease of interest to the medical profession in general and to psychiatry in particular.

Two ventures into industrial medicine are also worth noting. In 1860 Dr. I. Addison Freeman of Orange reported on "Mercurial Disease Among Hatters," referring to over one hundred cases that showed characteristics of mercurial salivation and stomatitis (inflammation of the membranes of the mouth) among hat-finishers in Orange, Newark, Bloomfield, and Millburn. He noted the need for proper ventilation. In 1864 Dr. John Stevenson reported on the "emphysematous state" of the lungs (the dilation of certain air passages) and the typical condition of the heart that were characteristic of glass-blowers.

The scientific interests of the profession are also to be discerned in the activities of smaller groups than the State Society.* References have already been made to

* In 1816 there were five county societies in existence—as adjuncts of the State Society—and by 1880 there were twenty such county groups. After the creation of the Cape May Society in 1885 every county had its own organization. Local societies appeared on the scene as early as 1835 when the Newark Medical Association was established. It was followed by an Essex Medical Union in 1859, a Trenton Medical Association about 1876, and an Orange Mountain Medical Society in 1884.

papers presented before the Burlington, Hudson, and Mercer County groups. The Essex County Society heard 48 papers in the period from 1820 to 1865, mostly discussions of particular diseases. In 1859 an Essex Medical Union met in the homes of members and exchanged "interesting cases," presented pathological specimens, and discussed any medical subject brought up.

One of the most interesting ventures was the New Jersey Academy of Medicine found in 1874. Originated by several prominent members of the Medical Society of New Jersey, its purposes were mainly scientific. It even planned a museum and a library, and obtained a charter which granted it authority to hold dissections. There are records of scientific sessions of the Academy in Newark, and there are announcements of monthly meetings, in Jersey City, until 1908.

The Academy had not been the first group permitted to dissect in the state. The Hudson County Pathological Society was incorporated in 1871 and its members given the right to hold dissections. The next year this right was extended to any chartered medical society in Hudson County, and a Jersey City Pathological Society remained in existence until 1883. Oddly, the State Society failed in its attempt to get a state-wide law permitting dissections when it sought one in 1887. One was finally obtained in 1895, but it was effective for only four years.

MEDICAL PUBLICATION

The formation of medical libraries and the issuance of medical publications are two other indications of medical progress. Attempts to establish libraries met with no appreciable success, on either the local or state level; the first successful medical library in New Jersey had to await the next century.* In publications, the State's

* The Monmouth Society had a "library" from 1822 to 1835; the Essex Society had one from 1830 to 1866; a suggested state medical library was not approved by the State Society in 1851.

record is a better one. In 1859 the Medical Society of New Jersey began to publish its transactions annually, and later decided to publish all its proceedings, going back to 1766. There is thus a complete record of the Society and the progress of the profession in its annual *Transactions*. These continued until 1904 when the present monthly *Journal* of the Society was begun.

Before 1859 the transactions of the State Society had been published in what was called *The New Jersey Medical Reporter, and Transactions of the New Jersey Medical Society*, a journal that was started in Burlington in 1847 by Joseph Parrish. The journal gained a national reputation and after its sale to Philadelphia interests in 1864 became the *Medical and Surgical Reporter*. Finally, there was the *Country Practitioner* published at Beverly by Dr. E. P. Townsend from 1879 to 1881. It was a lively journal, but disappeared when its editor moved to the city and then wandered off to the West.

SURGERY

Just as slow and tortuous as was the advance of medicine, so was the advance of surgery rapid and almost precipitous. Surgery depended on the oldest of the medical sciences, anatomy, and on the more recent advances in pathology. Its march to success followed a pragmatic course: anesthetics, antisepsis, asepsis, and new operative techniques that worked when put to the test; surgery did not have to wait for the development of bacteriology, physiology, and pharmacology.

The basic idea of asepsis was apparently recognized in New Jersey rather early. In 1848, at the end of the same decade in which Oliver Wendell Holmes and Ignaz Semmelweis had done their work with puerperal fever, one commentator noted that "the simultaneous occurrence of erysipelas and puerperal peritonitis" had led him to be concerned for his laboring patient when he was called to her bedside from a patient with erysipelas. "Under the apprehension that there might be some danger of communicating the disease," manual examinations were "as few and rapid as circumstances would justify . . . but . . . the hands were necessarily brought into contact with the mucus [sic] coat." However, although his hands "had been thoroughly washed," the doctor reported that the mother barely escaped with her life from puerperal fever, and the infant died a few weeks later of erysipelas.

It has been said that it took about two decades to get Joseph Lister's teachings (1860's) completely accepted in the United States. In New Jersey the comment was made in 1879 that Lister's "anti-septic" techniques had changed hospitals from charnel houses to health resorts. But new ideas often take hold slowly, and in 1884 surgeon Edward J. Ill of Newark, reporting seven successful ovariotomies, thought it necessary to remark that "all operations were done under strictly antiseptic precautions." In these cases, a carbolized spray had been used, and the silk ligatures had been previously boiled for one hour in a 6 per cent solution of carbolic acid. "On the evening prior to the operation, all instruments were soaked in absolute alcohol." In 1874, too, the idea of asepsis was well enough in vogue (or perhaps was still so little in vogue as to require special mention) for two physicians to note the value of washing the needle and syringe after injections. One attributed the lack of abscesses after injection to the "extra care in cleaning the needles immediately after each use in hot water."

Similarly with anesthetics. The introduction of ether into surgical use occurred in the 1840's, with the famous operation at the Massachusetts General Hospital taking place on October 16, 1846. This event, and accounts of subsequent successful uses of ether in the United States and abroad and the techniques used, were reported to the State Society at its meeting a year later. The report led the Standing Committee to agree that there could "exist no doubt as to the availableness of this prevention of pain," but elicited the warning that its use in New Jersey had had unpleasant results and that extreme caution in its use was necessary. By 1849 the Standing Committee was suggesting that the physicians of the State give "more consideration" to the use of "etherization" in childbirth, and by 1860 anesthesia was in general use. Chloroform was in use in the sixties; bromide of ethyl was a subject of discussion in the late seventies; cocaine was used in ophthalmology in 1866, not long after it was introduced. In 1884 New Jersey physicians were trying rectal anesthesia in Orange and Newark hospitals, and were predicting that unless its disadvantages (prolonged prostration, intestinal irritation) could be overcome, "the era of rectal anesthesia will be short."

The nineteenth century saw many remarkable incursions into the live human body. At the beginning of the century, excision of accessible tumors, lithotomy, amputations, and fractures were the extent of surgical activity; by the end of the century, the brain, the thyroid, the stomach, the kidney, the appendix, the intestines, the ovary, the uterus, the prostate, and other internal organs and organ systems were being exposed to the surgeon's knife.

This rapid progress was much in evidence in New Jersey. New Jersey surgeons began probing into the abdomen as early as 1860, ventured into it rather rarely for fifteen years, and then went in with impunity, for those were the days of "heroic and haphazard surgery." One critic, who referred to the "craze for laparotomies" (opening of the abdomen), nevertheless contended, "It has been discovered that there are men [in New Jersey] who can make a diagnosis . . . remove an offending uterus, as well as irritating ovaries, successfully. . . . Abdominal walls are no longer a barrier to an inquisitive surgeon." In 1860 Dr. C. Morrogh of New Brunswick reported the construction of an artificial anus "by cutting through the abdominal walls over the region of the coecum [and stitching] the gut . . . to the edges of the wound." In 1865 Dr. James B. Cutter of Newark removed an ovarian tumor "in the presence of many of the Faculty of this and New York City." Dr. Edward J. Ill of Newark, summarizing, in 1891, the activity in the State, listed at least twelve operations between 1865 and 1875, mostly for ovarian tumors and Caesarean sections. Between 1882 and 1891, however, he reported that Dr. C. S. Van Riper of Paterson listed 22 operations, mostly ovarian and uterine surgery, but including also gallstone, kidney, hernia, and others. Other surgeons reported similar although less numerous cases, but the records of Dr. Ill himself are most revealing. Between 1881 and 1891 Dr. Ill opened the abdomen at least 96 times, only twice on males.

Obviously, genito-urinary surgery was becoming quite common. Dr. Ill's operations for the most part were for the removal of tumors and cysts, for the removal of the Fallopian tubes and ovaries, and for the ventrofixation of the uterus. But other gynecological procedures were in use. The Sims operation for vesico-vaginal fistula was performed by Dr. J. D. Brumley (with five "assistants") in Newark in 1862, and the essay of Dr. G. H. Balleray of Paterson in 1881 on "Laceration of the Cervix Uteri" indicated that a great deal of progress had been made in gynecology.

Surgery, however, had not yet reached a high degree of safety. Too often one finds a careful account of a delicate operation after which the patient died. But as surgery progressed, the chances of success increased. Of the twelve operations referred to by Dr. Ill for the decade from 1865 to 1875, only one patient is recorded as having recovered. Dr. Ill's own case history is quite different, however: he reported 73 recoveries or cures. There is no way of telling how long his "recoveries" lasted, but about one out of four of his patients died postoperatively.

These deaths, and the factors that accounted for most of them—shock, hemorrhage, "exhaustion," peritonitis, septicemia, and the inexperience and errors of the surgeons—made it quite obvious that surgery still had far to go. It needs to be noted, also, that there were those who were critical of these heroic measures in gynecology. "The fact is that the desire to cut, twist, turn, amputate, electrolyze, and pessarize the uterus has amounted to almost a mania," said Dr. R. H. Page in 1879. Dr. Page was not alone in such criticisms.

Despite the attention in the literature to the "glorious progress" of abdominal surgery, other surgical activity of considerable interest took place in New Jersey. There was, for example, the intricate operation to excise a tumor from behind the nose and eye at Andover in 1868. Professor H. B. Sands of New York was called in to perform the operation, "a delicate and formidable one, never having been performed in this country, and but twice in Europe."

Other interesting cases and activities reported included, for example, the description by Dr. A. Clendinen of Bergen County of an apparatus for blood transfusion that he had developed (1878). A skin-grafting procedure was reported in 1885, in which bits of skin were planted on a patient's arm for a year, purportedly with success. In the same year the use of the laryngoscope in an operation for the removal of a throat papilloma was reported.

Writing in 1891, Dr. Ill lamented the fact that the proximity of New York and Philadelphia meant that New Jersey could not take a foremost rank in the surgical work of the country. Parochially—but there is little reason to question the verdict—Dr. Ill went on to "defy any state to show up a like report [on surgical work] that is better."

SPECIALIZATION IN MEDICINE

The nineteenth century saw the beginning of modern medical specialization as a concomitant of some of the significant developments of medicine: the acceptance of the idea of disease entities; the development of pathologic anatomy and its emphasis on diseases of specific organs and organ systems; the overall scientific growth of medicine that seemed to push forward the limits of knowledge infinitely and that introduced a new and complex technology. The same processes were obviously at work in New Jersey. The "men-midwives" of the eighteenth century had become the "obstetricians" of the nineteenth. In 1856 Dr. William Pierson of Orange presented a statistical report of his "obstetrical practice" that indicated that he had delivered 2,030 children in 28 years for an average of over 72 a year. In a "country obstetric practice" lasting 'many years," Dr. Charles Hasbrouck reported in 1871 that he had handled 1135 cases of labor and a total of 1151 births. The transition from "man-midwife" to "obstetrician" and later to "gynecologist" was something of a professional joke at the time, but it is in fact an illustration of the changes taking place in medicine, science, and technology.

The separation of medicine and surgery followed the same pattern. Surgery and medicine had had a long history of separation in Great Britain, but the exigencies of life in the New World could not permit such luxury. As we have seen, the general practitioner in North America was a practitioner of both medicine and surgery. In the words of one authority early in the nineteenth century, it was "difficult . . . to draw the line of distinction; surgery and physic are, particularly in this country, so closely connected, that an attendance on the lectures of the professors of Surgery, is very properly a prerequisite for a degree in Medicine." The general practitioner could well take care of the surgical needs of his patient early in the century when surgery was largely concerned with external or superficial conditions. But when surgery began to probe deeply and intricately, the ordinary practitioner might be more hesitant about using the knife and leave the work to the skill of the surgeon. Thus it is not surprising to find, as early as 1880, that there was a "Surgical Section" in the Camden County Medical Society.

Other specialists appeared on the scene. For example, Dr. Holden's work with the sphygmograph mentioned above indicates a growing interest in cardiology, and Dr. John W. Corson's work on the "Impulse of the Heart, as a Valuable Sign of Comparative Safety in the Use of Anaesthetics" (for the American Medical Association as early as 1855; for the New Jersey Society in 1879) indicates the development of an interest in anesthesiology. Dr. Henry L. Coit's interest in certified milk was a concomitant of his interest in pediatrics. The advent of hospitals, to be considered later, and the clinic system also added to the growing specialization. At St. Michael Hospital in Newark in 1872, there were clinics on the skin, the throat and chest, and the eye and ear.

The last-named became the specialty that was to arouse the greatest interest in New Jersey. In 1860 Dr. J. Henry Clark presented "A Glance at My Case Book," in which he reported on one hundred cases of otorrhea (discharge from the ear), discussed deafness, described his own improvement on an artificial tympanum (ear drum) and described three cases of affliction of the eye.

The highlight, however, was the opening of eye and ear clinics in Newark. The one at St. Michael Hospital, under Dr. Charles J. Kipp, came into existence about 1870, and a Newark City Eye and Ear Infirmary, a free institution, was said to have been "reopened" in 1874 by Dr. M. H. C. Vail. The latter infirmary seems not to have had a long or continuous existence, but a Newark Eye and Ear Infirmary began operation in 1880 with Dr. Kipp as its chief after a dispute at St. Michael.

Newark, though behind Boston, Philadelphia, and Baltimore in time, must indeed have become an important ophthalmologic and otologic center. In 1880 St. Michael reported that it had treated 14,090 patients since its inception and the Newark Eye and Ear Infirmary reported 11,999 cases (57,758 visits) in its first four years. In 1881 the latter reported having performed 301 operations in eleven months, 273 on the eye, and in 1883 it reported 20 cataract operations. As might be expected, these clinics became centers for the training of specialists. The Standing Committee of the State Society insisted that the opportunities afforded at Newark were "not surpassed anywhere." Dr. Kipp particularly published widely and became nationally known. He was to become the president of both the American Ophthalmological

Society in 1907 and the American Otological Society in 1908. At St. Michael the success of the clinics led to talk that they might become the nucleus of a medical school.

Indeed, the success of these Newark infirmaries apparently was reflected in the opening of similar infirmaries in Paterson (1883) and in Trenton (1884 or 1885).

A description of the rise of the specialist in New Jersey cannot disregard the fact that New Jersey conformed to the general pattern also with regard to the dislike, if not the animosity, with which the specialist was greeted by the general practitioner. For the most part, the antagonism was based on economic considerations—the specialist cut into the business of the local practitioner and was so unscrupulous, his critics charged, that he would consult with anyone, even with irregular practitioners. Occasionally, too, one heard the comment that overspecialization was dangerous, or that frequently the general practitioner was competent to deal with the problem without outside help. The trend could not be halted however; specialization and science marched on together.

V

ORGANIZED MEDICINE
IN THE NINETEENTH CENTURY

T HE SAME CONCERN with medical economics and professional identity that brought the New Jersey Medical Society into existence in 1766 continued to prevail in the nineteenth century. Fee bills, for example, were common through most of the century. The Burlington County Society provided for one in 1829. A Newark Medical Association, formed in 1835, adopted a fee table which was revised in 1857 at greatly increased rates. The State Society adopted one the next year, and another in 1874. In 1864 and 1868 the Hunterdon County Society promulgated such bills. In 1883 a local group of physicians in Trenton, published its fee bill in the newspapers. But how effective these were is open to question. The *Country Practitioner* in 1880 called them "humbug" and contended that no physician was governed by them. Yet the State Society promulgated a new "Fee Table" in 1896.

Collection of fees remained bad; the doctor, in the country especially, had to be prepared to accept his payment in kind, and often had to see his bills go unpaid. In Hunterdon, Dr. Cornelius Larison's accounts for 1868 indicated that 11 per cent of his $6400 practice was not paid. In 1847 the District Society of Gloucester decided to keep a "Black Book" listing the names of delinquent patients, and the members pledged themselves to insist upon payment in advance and a promise to pay the creditor doctor if called by a person in the black book.

As early as 1853 the Burlington Society resolved to present bills at the termination of a case or within one month, although in Hunterdon County a six-month period was decided upon in the 1860's.

Of greater concern to organized medicine, however, was the licensing of physicians. Beset on the one hand by sectarianism and quackery of all sorts, and on the other by a social milieu so individualistic as to be disturbed by the granting of special privileges of any kind, the profession floundered about seeking a working formula.

Starting in 1816, the power of examination and licensing of physicians passed from the courts to the organized profession. The locus of control varied from time to time. First, county societies had the power (1816); then county boards of censors were created under the State Society with the former examining and the latter granting the license (1818); then three district boards of censors (East, Middle, and West) were established (1830); but no arrangement proved entirely satisfactory. In 1851 the legislature exempted from the licensing laws graduates of five New York and Philadelphia medical schools and in 1854 extended this exemption to graduates of any medical school which met certain minimal requirements; the long campaign of the "pseudo-practitioners" which began at least as early as 1832 had begun to bear fruit. New Jersey, the first state to regulate the practice of medicine, and one of only four or five to have such laws in the 1840's, became the last to emasculate or repeal them. The Era of the Common Man had finally come to New Jersey. By 1864 the State Society had decided to join the trend, and apparently acquiesced in the revision of its charter that left it solely a professional society, with power to grant medical degrees,* but no power to examine or

* Granted in 1825 and which it still possesses.

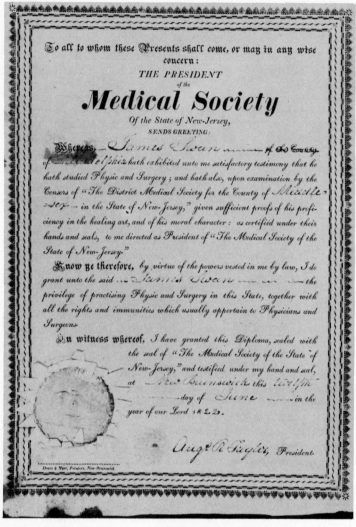

The medical license of James Swan, 1822
Rutgers University Library

license. The statute provided no alternative, and until the establishment of the first State board of medical examiners in 1890, the registration of a medical diploma with a county clerk was the only legal requirement to practice in the State. The regulars, for a time at least, were convinced that regulation was both ineffective and unnecessary, and that, with the Society regulating its own membership, the "distinction between the regular and irregular" was never more clearly noted by the public.

Indeed the door, never tightly closed, was now fully open to the sectarian and the quack. The "irregular bred pretenders to the healing art," prohibited by statute in 1830 from "practicing their deceptions and imposing upon the ignorance and credulity of their fellow citizens," were now virtually without restraint. Even after 1880, when a law provided that each practitioner must register with the county clerk a diploma from any "legally chartered" medical school, the great mushrooming of such schools—some only diploma mills—in Philadelphia, especially, made a mockery of the diploma.

In 1866 the Society reported that there were 596 "regular" practitioners and 151 "irregulars" in the State. The "irregulars" numbered ·60 homeopaths, 36 eclectics, six Thomsonians, five Botanics, six "electricians," five cancer doctors, five clairvoyants, three root doctors, two of the "Swedish movement," two hydropaths, one Indian doctor, and one "inhalation" practitioner. Two more were listed simply as "Quacks," and 17 were not classified or practiced no particular system. Of these, 21 were females, all of them, the report ungallantly contended, "of the class known as the progressive bloomer kind, spiritualists and infidels."

New Jersey was no different from the rest of the country in this multiplicity of sects. Nor did these irregulars always seek to pass themselves off for anything more than they were; virtually the same categories as those above were listed in the Newark City Directory from the 1860's to the 1880's. Sometimes, too, a cult would surround itself with a rationale and an appearance of legality, if not respectability. The Morristown Hydropathic Institution was established in Montclair in 1845 by a George T. Dexter. Dr. Dexter put out *The Fountain or Hydropathic Journal* in which he expounded on the effects of immersion or cold shower bath on the circulation and on the restoration of body function. In 1850 Dr. Dexter obtained a charter for the Parkeville Hydropathic Institute and apparently moved his operations to Gloucester County. In 1852 there were a "water-cure" doctor and hospital in Orange, and in 1868 the New Jersey Medical Electric Institute was incorporated, apparently with headquarters at Hoboken. This last group sought to practice and instruct in the art of curing disease by the use of electricity.

The Thomsonians, Botanics, and Eclectics, were, however, of a different sort. Started as "a mass of uneducated, fanatical patent-right holders," these groups developed schools, societies, and a literature and sought to imitate the institutional arrangements of the regulars. Their therapeutics differed from that of the regulars in their refusal to use mineral or alkaloidal drugs; theirs was a "non-poisonous," largely botanical system of medication. New Jersey seemed well supplied with this group of practitioners, and New Jersey men joined in 1852 in the formation of the Middle States Reformed Medical Society. Slowly, the distinction between the botanics and the regulars, all of whom used botanicals, seemed to disappear. A case in point is Dr. Morton Robinson of Newark. Robinson began to practice as a botanic physician in Newark in 1851 or 1852, although he did not graduate from the botanical Metropolitan Medical College of New York until 1854. He was listed among the botanics in the Newark City Directory from 1851 to 1871, and although he was president of the Eclectic Medical Society of the State of New Jersey (founded in 1873) in 1877, his directory listing was shifted to the rubric "allopath" in 1872. From 1883 to 1894 he was described simply as "physician and surgeon."

The homeopathic physician, whose name came from the principle of *similia similibus curantur*—treat like with like—and who believed in minute doses, went through a little different history. (In contradistinction to homeopathy, the regular practice became known as allopathy, that is, treatment with remedies causing effects different from those of the disease.) Some of the homeopaths, "classical men, moral, virtuous citizens" nonetheless, had turned from allopathy to homeopathy, and having originally met the requirements of licensure were still to be permitted (in 1848) "guarded medical intercourse" with the allopaths. It was hoped that they might eventually be restored "to the pale of the orthodox church." Others, however, had begun their careers outside the pale, and were to be kept outside. But the homeopaths, like the eclectics, attained increasing professional respectability as they established their own medical schools and their own societies. In 1877 the New Jersey State Homeopathic Society was incorporated and the homeopath given "all the benefits and privileges of any duly licensed physician and surgeon."

The initial reaction of the allopaths to the eclectics and homeopaths was, as just suggested, that of prohibiting intercourse with them. Later there was recourse to law and the courts, but this did not always prove to be good for public relations. Their reactions were based on theoretical grounds, on the honest belief that these men were ignorant charlatans, endangering their patients, and on the desire to protect their own interests. But as the two leading sects kept "pace with the advances in regular medicine," they were increasingly brought within the pale of the regular medical profession. In 1884 a New Jersey statute defined the term homeopathic so as to restrict its use to regularly trained or professionally accepted (by recognized Societies) practitioners. At about the same time, the model Act proposed by the American Medical Association provided that no applicant be excluded from an examination because of his adherence to a special system of practice. When the first State Board of Medical Examiners was created in 1890, it was to consist of five "old school" practitioners, three homeopathic practitioners, and one eclectic practitioner. The idea of a *State* board had originated with the Medical Society of New Jersey at least five years earlier, but a suggestion of the Society that two separate boards be instituted, one for the allopaths and one for the homeopaths went unheeded. Indeed, the 1890 act, rather realistically provided that all candidates, eclectic, homeopathic, and allopathic be given the same examination except on materia medica and therapeutics. In 1908 the Camden County Medical Society elected a homeopath to membership, and as medicine itself advanced as a science, the homeopaths and eclectics forsook their monistic theories and practices.

By 1881 the regular medical profession was no longer certain of the value of laissez faire in medical practice and was ready to recommend new departures. It took a long time, however, to effect the required legislation. The State Board of Medical Examiners was not provided for until 1890, and the statute gave no special power or privileges to the State Society. Applicants for the examination were required (as of 1894) to have a medical diploma from an American college acceptable to the Board, or a diploma or license permitting him to practice in a foreign country, in addition to certain other specified requirements as to the length of study. The century was to end with the examination and licensing of physicians required—but under the aegis, not of the professional organization, but of the State government.

MEDICAL EDUCATION

Examination and license alone, however, did not assure the quality of medical practice; the training of the physician was of prime importance. In this respect New Jersey fared well, for most of her practitioners were "regulars" who had graduated from reputable medical schools. The Standing Committee of the State Medical Society estimated in 1866 that there was one regular physician for each 1251 of population, while there was one "quack" for every 4450. A census taken of the medical profession in Camden County in 1851 counted 24 regulars, one regularly graduated homeopath, one non-graduated homeopath, and one botanical practitioner who made no claim to being an educated physician. Twenty years later the regulars were still in the great majority, atlhough the others were more numerous (33 regulars, 13 homeopaths, 5 eclectics). Moreover, in Camden (1846-1886), Hunterdon (1822-1853), and Burlington (1866) counties, the records indicated that most licensed practitioners had "graduated respectably in some one of the recognized medical institutions of the country."

The growing preponderance of medical school graduates in the ranks of New Jersey physicians should not lead the observer to overestimate the knowledge and abilities of these men. In the first place, the figures just cited refer to regularly licensed physicians and members of the county medical societies—by and large the best of the practitioners. Moreover, medical degrees were not difficult to come by. Witness the roster of physicians for Camden County in 1880: 25 were graduates of the University of Pennsylvania, 17 of Jefferson, eleven of Hahnemann, seven of the Pennsylvania College of Homeopathic Medicine, three from Penn University, two from the Acad. Terrae Mariae (University of Maryland), and one each from Harvard College, Dartmouth College, American Veterinary College, Philadelphia College, Philadelphia University, Pennsylvania College, Eclectic Medical College, "Ac. Neo Eborareosis" (New York University?), Northwestern University, and University of Glasgow.

In addition, medical training was not always of the highest quality even at the better medical schools. Short terms, minimal requirements of attendance at lectures, meager library resources, limited clinical facilities and requirements, and easy graduation were the common conditions at mid-century. Matters did not improve too much in the second half of the century as the Flexner Report in 1910 was to make clear; but the situation was exacerbated by the mushrooming of medical schools of all descriptions and the appearance of diploma mills. The process was aided by the ease with which charters were available, as in Pennsylvania, and the absence of effective controls, in New Jersey as elsewhere.

New Jersey was to be caught up in this maelstrom of medical education, too. At the College of New Jersey in Princeton, a second attempt to found a medical department in the period from 1818 to 1824 came to an end with the death of the man who was to be professor of medicine. Queen's College (later Rutgers) at New Brunswick awarded medical degrees in 1792 and 1793, from 1812 to 1816, and from 1827 to 1835. A few of these were honorary; most were a result of studies under, and on the recommendation of, first, Nicholas Romayne, then David Hosack and others at the Rutgers Medical College, all in New York. There is no record of medical instruction at the New Brunswick campus; the medical faculty of the college was simply the New York group. The activity at Queen's College met the approbation of the Medical Society of New Jersey, but came to an end when the State of New York refused to recognize an out-of-state degree for studies undertaken in New York, and Hosack switched to Geneva College. A suggestion in 1872 that a college of medicine and surgery might develop out of the clinic at St. Michael Hospital in Newark, affiliated with Seton Hall College, did not materialize. In 1888 the proposed law intended to remove any remaining obstacles to dissection, was obviously worded so as to permit the development of medical schools in the State. This, too, was abortive.

The proliferation of medical sects and medical schools did not pass New Jersey by. The notorious John Buchanan "located" one of his bogus colleges at his farm in Haddonfield, and in the decade of the 1870's issued diplomas from his mythical University of Medicine and Surgery of Haddonfield, New Jersey, also apparently known as Livingston(e) University. There is a reference to a Hygeo-Therapeutic Institute that cannot be traced. The Eclectic Medical and Surgical College of the State of New Jersey, chartered in 1870, did begin operation in Jersey City in 1888. At the end of that year it changed its name to the Medical and Surgical College of the State of New Jersey. In 1889 there were said to be 22 matriculants in the college and 12 graduates, but the venture was scarcely a bona fide institution. The State Board of Medical Examiners prevailed upon the legislature in 1891 to repeal the 1870 charter. Finally, there was a Central University of Medicine and Surgery, also located in Jersey City, incorporated in 1898 and still technically in existence in 1901. Its fate is unknown.

It is clear that as the nineteenth century progressed, attendance at medical schools became an adjunct to, rather than a replacement for preceptorship. Of the 44 members of the Medical Society of New Jersey who died between 1865 and 1871, for example, 36 had attended medical schools, and 34 had had preceptorships. Of the 52 who died between 1885 and 1890, all but one had had a medical school affiliation, and 32 had studied under a preceptor.

It is also interesting to note that undergraduate college training prior to medical studies was not yet significant. The problem was more basic: to be sure that the medical student had at least a high school education. About 1869 the head of the Harvard Medical School replied to President Charles Eliot's proposal that a written examination for entrance be required, with the statement: "More than half of them [Harvard medical students] can barely write. Of course they can't pass written examinations." This may have been an exaggeration, but the account books of Sweet and Robinson, Newark practitioners for about half the century, are replete with such gems as "neuraligy," "purifien Balson," "redusen" (for reducing), and "farther" (for father). No wonder that the Medical Society of New Jersey, always interested in the prior education of apprentices, recommended, in 1883, that anyone contemplating the study of medicine in the State who was not a high school graduate or better should be examined in an imposing array of classical and humanistic subjects.

VI

THE SANITARY MOVEMENT

M EDICINE HAS RECEIVED her most glorious renown in
the prevention not in the cure of disease," stated Dr.
George T. Welch of Keyport in 1884. Here was a recognition of the fact that, whatever the decline in the incidence of such diseases as cholera, typhus, yellow fever,
malaria, and typhoid, it was not, in the nineteenth century, a medical accomplishment arising out of the demonstration of the germ theory of disease and the consequent
development of vaccines and antitoxins. Smallpox vaccine antedated the nineteenth-century developments in
the germ theory of disease; by the end of the century only
a few diseases, like diphtheria, rabies, tetanus, and an-
thrax were successfully treated by the new biological
therapeutics that reflected the new scientific knowledge,
although a great deal of experimentation was taking place
and many false starts were being made.

The conquest of disease and general improvement in
mortality rates that began in the late nineteenth century
reflected a great deal more than the new scientific advances in medicine. The increasing availability and use
of hospital facilities was also involved, and general social
progress, better standards of living, improved food supplies, increasing educational opportunities all had a share.
But a goodly share of the credit must be given to the
work of the sanitarians.

A variety of motives have been ascribed to the men
and women who sought to police the community into

cleanliness and good health. One writer suggests the influence of the eighteenth-century philosophical yearnings for a return to nature and simplicity—the social conditions of overcrowding, squalor, and filth brought on disease; the natural conditions of fresh air, hygiene, and cleanliness would prevent disease. Others suggest more simply a growing humanitarianism derived on the Continent from a benevolent despotism (that led there to a "medical police"), and derived in Britain from a "new philosophy" largely individualistic and utilitarian.

New Jersey, of course, reflected the British experience, and her physicians were aware of the relation between social environment and disease. Diphtheria, it was said in 1864, occurred more generally and most fatally among the ill-fed, ill-clothed, and improperly housed. Immigrants, patronizingly described as "educated to filth," were particularly in need of instruction and coercion. Thus Dr. Ezra M. Hunt of Metuchen, who was to become the leading sanitarian in New Jersey, citing the work of the great British sanitarian Edwin Chadwick, pointed out in 1867 the need for and desirability of elevating the masses. Improve the conditions of health and vice will abate, he argued; moral and mental elevation would follow physical elevation. A year earlier the Medical Society had been exhorted to make it plain to the public that health was also economically advantageous to society.

The movement for sanitary reform was sometimes spearheaded by medical men, and where the original impulse came from laymen and philanthropists, as it often did, there were always medical men who soon joined in the crusade. As the century progressed, moreover, sanitation, like medicine itself, became more scientific, and medical men played increasingly significant roles. Along with men like Dr. Hunt, a prime mover in the founding of the State Board of Health, there were others like Dr. Henry L. Coit of Newark, who achieved international fame with the introduction and promotion of certified milk (1887-1892).

The motivations of New Jersey sanitarians may have been humanitarian and utilitarian, but it was soon evident that only public authority could properly police the public health. Under municipal authority, cleanup campaigns, the paving of streets, the improvement of drainage, the construction of sewers, the cleaning of privies, the elimination of pig sties, and such were resorted to. Fumigation and disinfection were practiced, and quarantines were established. Such methods often proved effective. In 1861 it was claimed that the deaths in Newark increased by only 6 per cent because of such measures while the population increased 9½ per cent, and the next year the paving of streets and removal of garbage were credited with lowering the malaria rate there. Union County claimed a drop from 380 cases of scarlet fever in 1883 to 67 cases in 1885 because of its sanitary measures, and in 1885 Atlantic City credited the absence of typhoid fever to the effectiveness of its campaign. For the most part, however, the measures taken were after the fact: Newark, Elizabeth, and Camden cleaned up after the cholera outbreak of 1866; Camden took measures after a smallpox outbreak in 1872.

It is evident from the record, however, that the growth of New Jersey cities very rapidly outdistanced their efforts at sanitation. In only two or three years between 1859 and 1878 did the death rate in Newark fall to 20 or less per 1000—the top figure calculated as "proper and necessary." In most of the other years it ranged from over 25 per 1000 to a high of over 32 in 1872. In 1877 the death rate in Newark of 29.96 per thousand, by one estimate, was higher than that of New York, Boston, Richmond, Philadelphia, Providence, St. Louis, and San Francisco. In 1884 the city had 178 miles of streets and only 50 miles of sewers. Only one-third of the houses had sewer connections, and two-thirds had privies and cesspools. It was calculated that two hundred thousand pounds of excreta went into the soil of the city daily, and what cleaning up was done was done by the dipper and bucket system. Trenton, in 1880, attained the distinction of being called "the dirtiest city in the country." In Camden in 1885 an outbreak of diphtheria with a mortality rate of 50 per cent hit a school where "little attention had been given towards securing the health and comfort of the pupils."

WATER AND SEWAGE

Knowledge of bacterial causation was hardly essential to the awareness of the direct relationship between filth and contamination and disease. Dr. John Snow's incrimination of the Broad Street pump in London in 1854 had shown this. New Jersey physicians in 1863 spoke of "Kensington Diarrhea," which resulted from drinking water from the Kensington Water Works in Philadelphia. In 1879 typhoid fever was being called "water poison," and in 1883 Passaic was troubled with what was locally called "water cholera."

Basic to the problem was the disposal of waste materials. For the most part only the larger communities built sewers, but, as has just been noted, the privy and the cesspool were common in the cities. When sewers were built, the immediate effect seemed to be salutary. In Camden, for example, in 1869, it was said that the inhabitants "cheerfully bear the additional tax imposed upon them," because they were so pleased with the results. However, sewers were soon under attack. There were those who contended that seepage from them merely made the sewers continuous cesspools. More important was the contamination of water supplies by the short-sighted (perhaps unavoidably since there were no alternatives at the time) construction which emptied the sewers into the same rivers from which the water supplies were obtained. Thus Newark and Jersey City discovered in the 1870's that their Passaic River water was foul to the taste and smell and dangerous to the health. Upstream the new industries were pouring off arsenic, dyes, acids, and such into the stream. Upstream sewerage systems and cesspools from the cities and towns drained into the river. But worst of all, it was discovered that twice every 24 hours the tide carried the sewage of Newark from the point of its downstream entry into the Passaic, back up the river beyond the intakes of the Jersey City and Newark water supplies. "Pestilential! We are drinking foul sewage water," screamed the *Jersey City Sunday Eagle* in 1887. Moreover, the State geologist and chemist demonstrated that Newark's wells, from which about 55 per cent of the city's population got their water in 1877, were even more contaminated and more dangerous than the river water. Both cities built new upland water supplies with salutary results on the typhoid fever rate. In 1898 and 1899, however, Newark was again struck by the disease when Passaic water was brought into the water supply. Despite warnings to boil the water when this happened—by intention—in February, 1899, there were 378 cases (43 fatal) of typhoid fever in Newark in March and April. Camden, too, had faced a similar problem in the late 1880's when sewage from both Camden and Philadelphia was being virtually forced into her water supply.

Clearly the need for water purification in New Jersey was great and may in part account for New Jersey's outstanding position in the history of water purification devices and techniques. From the first charcoal, sand, and gravel filter in the country at Elizabeth in 1855, to the impetus given to chlorination by its adoption at the Boonton Reservoir of the Jersey City Water Works in 1908, New Jersey played a much more significant role in pioneering and invention in this connection than is usually acknowledged. Despite some gains, final success in providing pure water did not take place until the twentieth century, however.

BOARDS OF HEALTH

The work of the sanitarians in New Jersey seems to have been taken up by the physicians and the Medical

Society from the start. In 1849 a committee of the Society was appointed to "inquire into the necessity of a more complete system of law in respect to public health, particularly regarding vaccination." Four year later another committee thoroughly investigated the State statutes, and although it found a total of 174 laws affecting health in some way, it concluded that "the health laws of our State are exceedingly meager and inefficient." The Committee recommended in particular that attention be paid to ventilation of classrooms, ventilation and sanitation of workshops (the northern workman who was fired when he became ill or disabled was much worse off than the slave whose master protected his health, the Committee noted), and the draining of marshes, and that vaccination be "absolutely required by law."

In 1866 a new committee was created on the initiative, and then under the chairmanship, of Dr. Ezra M. Hunt. The next year Dr. Hunt delivered a discourse before the Society that, stripped of its eloquence, presented a cogent plea for adequate legislation, professional medical assumption of responsibility, and the diffusion of information. He illustrated his talk with numerous specific examples of the victories of preventive medicine and indicated the record of New Jersey in comparison with other parts of the country. He pointed to the social and economic values of the prevention of disease and the preservation of health, and insisted that "sanitary science" was "no longer a subject for doubtful disputation." Philanthropy could not obtain more than limited results. Moral suasion was ineffective, and only the police power of the state or municipality could accomplish the desired ends. Only "the strong arm of the law," said a corroborating statement, could properly "turn out, clean out and purify and disinfect, and, if need be, quarantine."

The Committee brought the matter to the attention of the governor, and in 1866 a "Sanitary Commission" was created consisting of five physicians. The Commission had the authority to report and advise, but its recommendation of a general health law, though it received the governor's favorable attention, failed to pass.

The Sanitary Commission, under the chairmanship of Dr. Hunt, remained active, however, and, early in 1867, a communication to the governor on an expected invasion of Asiatic cholera (and the sanitary measures to be taken) received general newspaper coverage and proved that there was value in having such a commission. In 1875 a new Commission, created the year before and still under the chairmanship of Dr. Hunt, recommended a model law—a brief, fairly innocuous document that suggested that the Commission had had to decide to proceed slowly.

At this juncture the New Jersey Sanitary Association came into existence at an organization meeting held in Newark. Physicians were at the forefront, but engineers and others were also active. The Association was to become a major force not only in the promotion of scientific studies, but in supporting the program of sanitary reform.

It is thus probably not just coincidence that the law proposed by the Commission was enacted in 1877. At last the old Civil War style name disappeared in favor of "Board of Health." The new State Board of Health (the Committee's recommendation that it also be a Board of Vital Statistics was not followed) was empowered to "take cognizance," "make investigations," "gather information," "make inquiries and reports," and nothing else. The first substantive power given (1880) to the Board was that of being able to order, under certain conditions, the slaughter of animals with rinderpest or other contagious diseases. Little by little the duties of the Board increased in this fashion. In 1880 it was empowered to assist local boards of health, and even to expend funds in its studies in local areas; in 1882 it was charged with appointing analysts to determine the quality of kerosene. And so it went—in the 1880's some aspect of the sanitation program was regularly the subject of legislation.

In 1880, "An Act concerning the protection of the

public health and the record of vital facts and statistics relating thereto" set the pattern for the sanitary policing in the State.* The Act required every municipal government to provide for a board of health on which there were to be a keeper of vital statistics, a municipal physician, and a health inspector. The local boards were empowered, particularly, to eliminate nuisances and to provide for the free vaccination of indigent school children. Two years later the power of the local boards was spelled out more precisely and they were given authority to pass ordinances and prescribe penalties in a variety of the usual hygienic and sanitary areas. By 1886 the existing statutes were consolidated, after some difficulties over the jurisdiction of local and county health boards.

The Secretary of the State Board, still charged with the "superintendence" of the Board's powers, was now to receive a salary and was required to be a physician. The control of vital statistics was now an important part of his work and the State Board, in addition to its investigatory powers, was empowered to appoint and assign duties to inspectors. The powers of the local boards of health were detailed and augmented, and one can get a very good idea of the scope and fundamental importance of the work in sanitation from the enumeration of these powers. The local boards were involved with: enforcement of the laws on adulteration of food and drugs; definition and removal of nuisances; prevention of disease and contagion; regulation of slaughterhouses; regulation and removal of offensive matter; requiring the return of birth, marriage, and death records; establishing and regulating sanitary conditions in tenements and public buildings; regulation of sewage, garbage, and filth; regulation of cesspools and privies; regulation of house drainage and plumbing connections to sewers; protection of water supplies; imposition of isolation and quarantine; and the regulation of burials. The next year the Act was repassed

* The pattern had been set to some extent by local commissions and boards in Newark, Jersey City, Camden, Long Branch, and Hudson County, some as early as the 1850's.

with some technical rewording but with its chief significance in the increase of the investigatory powers of the State Board to cover state institutions and the designation of the Board as the Bureau of Vital Statistics.

Under these arrangements the municipalities passed detailed and comprehensive sanitary codes, Newark taking advantage of the new legislation almost immediately by promulgating such a code in 1888. The State Board itself took on an essentially educational function. Not only did it keep the various local agencies and interested individuals informed of their legal obligations, but a constant stream of reports, circulars, and monographs. issued out of the State office. The variety and scope of this informational and advisory literature almost defies classification: oysters, vital statistics, smallpox, drainage, carbonic acid in the air, the mouth cavity are but a small sampling of the subjects covered. Except for the addition of a State Bacteriological Laboratory in 1895, no significant change took place in the organization of public health in the State until the work of the State Board was placed under five divisions in 1908.

Throughout this whole history of the sanitary movement in New Jersey the name of Ezra Mundy Hunt looms large. A prime mover in obtaining the interest of the medical profession in sanitation, he was president of the Sanitary Commission in 1866 and of the State Health Commission in 1874. After a European trip with Dr. John Shaw Billings he returned to New Jersey to become the Secretary (that is, executive officer) of the Board and remained in that office for 16 years. He was a charter member of the American Public Health Association, which was organized in 1872 at a meeting in Long Branch, and in 1883 became its President. In 1874 he participated in the founding of, and became corresponding secretary to, the New Jersey Sanitary Association. In 1877 he was chairman of the American Medical Association Section of State Medicine and Public Hygiene. He wrote a great deal, and attained a reputation as an epidemiologist sufficient to gain him honorary membership in the Epidemiological Society of London in 1880 and to have been called one of the great pioneers in public health on the basis of his having "originated modern concepts of rural health services." One need only read his annual reports or note the many "circulars" that came out of his office to recognize how much New Jersey gained from his devotion to his professional career.

Vaccination and Quarantine

Mention has been made in another connection of the problems that arose with regard to vaccination. Since the sanitarians were involved in the prevention of disease, they ran a continuous campaign for compulsory vaccination. Free vaccine was frequently available for the indigent—there was a Vaccine Institute at Paterson, incorporated in 1831, which offered free vaccination, and there was a free Newark Dispensary at least as early as 1858—but physicians were being constantly exhorted not to neglect vaccination and to support compulsory vaccination laws. Although only Massachusetts and the cities of Baltimore, Providence, and New York were said to have "enforced vaccination," the Sanitary Commission asked for compulsory vaccination of all school children, free to the indigent in 1867. Only the last part was provided for, on a voluntary basis, and then not until 1880. An 1896 report stated that 21 per cent of the children enrolled in New Jersey schools were not vaccinated. Certain of the rural counties were especially remiss: well over half the school children in Warren, Sussex, and Cumberland, for example, were unvaccinated. Not until 1902 could a vaccination be required of all pupils and teachers by a school board, although Hudson County had a compulsory vaccination provision in its sanitary code in 1874.

Quarantine as a public-health device was essentially a post-Civil War phenomenon in New Jersey. There are early records of attempts to impose quarantine on incoming ships in 1799, but the gist of the statutes was to force

New Jersey citizens to abide by the quarantine statutes of New York and Pennsylvania. In 1812 a special quarantine law for ships coming into Perth Amboy was passed, and in 1857 the sheriffs of Monmouth and Middlesex counties were empowered to order the removal of infected ships beyond the territorial waters of the State. The last act made the erection of a quarantine hospital at Sandy Hook a misdemeanor—an issue which was to embroil New Jersey and New York again in 1867 and 1875. Legislation providing for inspection of vessels was enacted in 1871, 1882, and again in 1897, when a nominal "New Jersey Quarantine Service" operated by local officials was created.

The application of quarantine procedures to sick persons, however, ran into a new angle of the contagion controversy. In the 1860's and 1870's the anti-contagionists seemed to find support from the sanitarians. If there was contagion, then quarantine restrictions could do little, and were, besides, usually evaded. What was needed, therefore, was sanitation and ventilation: "internal sanitary arrangements . . . are the safeguards of nations."

The germ theory of disease changed all this. Quarantine measures became common in the 1880's. (The dispute over whether children were safer in or out of school started very early, however.) Paterson invoked quarantine measures in 1882, and the Newark Sanitary Code of 1888 promulgated what was to be the general pattern. Physicians were requested to report contagious diseases to the Board of Health, and it in turn could require isolation of the patient if it thought it necessary. The sick child was to be kept out of school and the premises placarded. Fumigation and disinfection of premises and clothes were also provided for. At the end of the century the nurse in the isolation ward of the Orange Memorial Hospital (two rooms, one for the patient and one for the nurse) was not permitted to write letters and could read only such books as could later be burned. The extent to which such measures might go is indicated by a circular issued by the Morristown Board of Health—undated, it is likely to be an early twentieth-century document—which required that any child under 16 years of age who came into town (except any passing through) was to be placed under quarantine for at least two weeks. Inspectors were to go through the town daily to seek new arrivals. It is indeed but recently that the attitudes toward quarantine, particularly with regard to school attendance, have changed.

VII

HOSPITALS AND NURSING

In 1830 PARIS WAS SAID to have no less than 30 hospitals housing some twenty thousand patients. In 1863, the Standing Committee of the Medical Society of New Jersey lamented that New Jersey had no hospital within its borders, "notwithstanding its wealth and resources, and its *needs*." The population of the State in 1860 had been placed at six hundred and seventy-two thousand. Again the nearness of the two metropolises meant that New Jersey continued to rely on facilities on the other sides of its river borders.

Aside from the suggestion of hospital facilities of a kind in Newark, Elizabethtown, Morristown, Amboy, Fort Lee, New Brunswick, and Trenton during the Revolution, and of special lazarets like the one in New Brunswick for canal workers who fell victims of cholera in 1832, there is little to indicate any interest in any kind of hospital facility in New Jersey until the 1850's. In the first half of the century and later, almshouses usually had some arrangements for the care of the incapacitated. The Newark almshouse in 1857 included among its inmates the old and infirm, lunatics, and idiots. A few years earlier the Newark poorhouse farm included a "hospital for infectious diseases." Cholera patients were sent there and accommodations were so meager that the authorities were "obliged to put . . . two in a bed." Later, accident cases were sent there, and the establishment was referred to as "the Newark Hospital."

In 1850 the citizens of Newark began to discuss building a hospital. The mortality rate among the sick-poor at the almshouse was not only too high, but the almshouse was in an unhealthful, low-lying location. Newark as a growing industrial city was troubled with an increasing number of industrial, traffic, and railroad accidents. A hospital was needed for these reasons and for surgical purposes. But a great deal of activity ended with the chartering of a "Newark Hospital" in 1857 that never materialized.

A similar situation developed in Jersey City, where a Hudson County Hospital was incorporated in 1861, and a building and medical staff were provided for. In 1874, however, the building was leased to a new group, but, in the meantime, in 1869, apparently on the initiative of the District Medical Society of Hudson County, Jersey City had established a Charitable Hospital and Dispensary by municipal ordinance. This hospital was originally connected with the city almshouse but was later separated to become the Jersey City Hospital. Probably New Jersey's oldest municipally owned hospital, from it have come the earliest hospital case reports in New Jersey (1870).

That the Jersey City institution was also a dispensary reflects the fact that the latter was another institution for the care of the poor that bore a direct relationship to the development of the hospital. There was in Newark a city dispensary "for the gratuitous relief of patients," at least as early as 1857, under the control of a Board of Health. In 1860 beds and other services were provided "for the accommodation of hospital patients," and the institution was referred to as the Dispensary and Hospital. In Newark this did not lead directly to the establishment of a hospital, for a city hospital was not provided for until 1882.* Then, under the control of the Committee on

* The hospital movement in Newark was probably slowed by the willingness of the Military Hospital there during the Civil War to handle civilians in an emergency. A rather large institution to which the sick and wounded were brought by ship by the hundreds, this hospital expanded its facilities as exigencies demanded. In 1862 it was reported that there were fifteen hundred sick and wounded in Newark. The hospital was discontinued at the end of the war.

Poor and Alms of the Common Council, a hospital was attached to the almshouse. Its medical staff served gratuitously, and, although the hospital provided for 75 patients, it accommodated only 25 to begin with. (In 1880 Newark had a population of 136,000.)

Both Orange and Camden, however, traveled the dispensary-to-hospital route more directly, in both places under philanthropic auspices. The Orange Memorial Hospital began as a dispensary in 1873 and moved into a hospital building in 1882, after a Ladies Auxiliary Society had raised a substantial amount of money. In Camden a group of physicians had established a dispensary in 1865, and when death, in 1874, ended the plans of Dr. Richard M. Cooper to turn this into a full-fledged hospital, his family bequeathed about two hundred and fifty thousand dollars for land and the building of a hospital. Unfortunately bad planning or the failure of the community to respond generously enough—altogether about fifty thousand dollars more was expended on the building—did not permit the actual opening of the hospital, named for its benefactors, until 1887. By that time the plumbing needed refitting!

The dispensary, it must be said, was more than the forerunner of the public hospital. Its more direct significance to health in the nineteenth century is pointed up by some statistics from the Newark Dispensary. In the years from 1876 to 1878 inclusive, it served 151,519 patients, issued 121,664 prescriptions, extracted 3855 teeth, and gave 627 vaccinations, a not inconsequential record in a city of less than 136,000. The poor—and there was obviously a great many of them—did not go completely uncared for.

Similar civic and humanitarian interests helped found hospitals elsewhere. In Newark the movement for a general hospital was taken up, after the collapse of the "Newark Hospital" movement, by the German community. After years of effort and the cooperation of 62 German clubs and societies, the "German Hospital" was dedicated in 1870. Despite the fact that its chief founder, Frederick A. Lehlbach, was a Lutheran pastor, and that the hospital was known from 1946 to 1952 as the Lutheran Memorial Hospital, it was a nonsectarian institution whose charter prohibited any religion discrimination. It is now the Clara Maass Memorial Hospital.

In Paterson a slightly different pattern evolved. There the idea for a nonsectarian general hospital was first conceived by the Minister's Association, but it was a group of women who formed themselves into a Hospital Association that carried out the idea. Their institution was referred to as the "Ladies Hospital" from its founding in 1871 until 1887. It is now the Paterson General Hospital.

It would be a mistake to assume from the foregoing that the hospital movement in New Jersey received its initial or most significant impetus from either governmental concern for the poor, or from the labors of individual physicians, philanthropists, or civic leaders.

A large segment of the hospital movement in New Jersey derived rather from deeply religious and sectarian motivations. In fact, the first volunteer hospital of which there is an unquestionable record—it is difficult to ascertain "firsts" both because the complete record has not been researched and because there were often gaps between "establishment" and actual commencement of operation—was probably that of St. Mary's Hospital in Hoboken. It was opened in 1863 by the Sisters of the Poor of St. Francis, a German order, and was to care for the sick and injured, that is, it was what would be called now a "short-stay" hospital. The same order, although more-or-less contemporary accounts refer to them as Sisters of Charity and Sisters of Mercy, established a dispensary in Newark, as well, in 1866 or 1867. This was open only in the afternoons, and the sisters made home calls at other times—visiting nurses, as it were. The sisters, dependent entirely upon donations, were able to open a house on Bleeker Street to accident cases in 1869. That year they moved to High Street, where their little 13-bed establishment became the St. Michael Hospital (originally and until recently, St. Michael's Hospital) with a bed capacity variously given as 150 in 1871 and 130 in 1873.

Even before St. Michael and the German hospitals were in operation, the Episcopalians in Newark had begun a small institution. In existence in 1865 and originally known as "St. Barnabas House," it was incorporated two years later as St. Barnabas Hospital and housed ten patients that year.

What happened in Hoboken and Newark was repeated elsewhere. In Paterson the Sisters of Charity founded St. Joseph's Hospital in 1867. Known to the community as the "Charity Hospital," St. Joseph's began inconspicuously in a small frame house. With no endowment, it typified the dependence of such institutions on the benevolence of their patrons and the self-sacrifice of their staffs. In Jersey City, St. Francis Hospital was started in 1869, although at one time it claimed an 1862 origin— a date which would give it priority over St. Mary's in Hoboken. In 1873 Christ Hospital came into existence in the same city, under the auspices of the Reverend Richard Abercrombie. He obtained the support of Episcopal clergymen in the establishment of what was first called the "Hudson County Church Hospital." In Trenton, another St. Francis Hospital was begun in 1869 with the arrival of three Sisters of St. Francis and a postulate. They erected a building which was dedicated in 1874— the year now given as the year of establishment of the hospital.

The sectarian basis of these institutions is evident from their charter provisions. The Roman Catholic Hospitals were placed under the government of church officials. The Episcopalian charters provided that "the moral and religious instruction of the inmates . . . be in conformity with the doctrine, discipline and worship of the Protestant Episcopal Church in the United States."

Yet this did not mean that these hospitals took care only of their own. Perhaps there is no more beautiful expression of the universality of Christian charity than the words of the first report of St. Joseph's Hospital: "It is the earnest prayer of the Sisters . . . that they may be able to afford asylum to every poor sufferer and that none may turn from their door to encounter, amidst strangers, hearts without pity and souls without love." The founders of Christ Hospital in Jersey City provided that "to all patients, the clergymen of such patients' denomination and choice, shall have free access daily for religious instruction and worship," and St. Michael Hospital denied allegations in 1873 that Protestant clergymen were not permitted to visit patients.

But the persistence of such rumors indicated that there were those in the community who took exception to sectarian hospitals. One of the less polite of these critics was the editor of the *Newark Daily Advertiser*. "Spare us the pretence of a general benediction when the purpose is propagandism," he wrote in 1870. "There is no such thing as evangelical small-pox or protestant typhoid, nor has the Scarlet Woman any special relations with scarlet-fever," he wrote again three years later. The editor did not belittle the accomplishment of St. Michael, St. Barnabas, or the German hospitals. He was campaigning for a secular city-supported hospital and was also objecting in principle to any tax support for a sectarian institution. A proposal in 1870 to appropriate $10,000 of municipal funds to St. Michael led him to declaim, "The quality of charity cannot be strained through the city treasury . . . let charity be charity—and let the city establish a hospital to meet its needs on a non-sectarian basis."

But as the campaign for a city hospital bogged down in Newark, the three hospitals there were accepting charity patients and receiving some recompense for doing so from the city. It will interest the modern hospital administrator to know that in 1875 the German and St. Michael hospitals were both requesting the city for higher allowances for such patients.

The significance of the sectarian hospital must, however, not be underestimated. The first four permanent general hospitals in the State each bore a Saint's name; then came the German Hospital, then still another sectarian hospital. Of the 17 hospitals that were in existence, projected, or chartered before 1875, only seven were

clearly nonsectarian. In the next decade, however, not
a single sectarian hospital was established, and in the
1890's only four more were established. By the end of the
century the total number of hospitals in existence reached
36. Of these only eleven had had discernible sectarian
origins.

Of the hospitals actually in existence and in some form
of operation before 1875, all were in four counties—
Hudson, Essex, Passaic, and Mercer. In Camden, Union,
Burlington, and Middlesex, the first hospitals were in
operation in the decade from 1876 to 1885, and by the
end of the century only rural Sussex, Warren, Hunterdon,
Ocean, Cape May, Gloucester, and Salem counties were
without hospitals.

Although this may seem to have been a rather rapid
growth of hospitals,* New Jersey was hardly overextended
in its hospital facilities. The Newark City Hospital, for
example, had to turn away patients in 1885. The total
number of hospitalized patients in the state on June 1,
1890, according to the United States Census, was 2941,
a small but not altogether inconsequential figure. Most
hospitals started out with very meager appointments and
were often no more than old dwellings turned into a few
bedrooms. St. Barnabas started out with secondhand beds
and a building without water closets. Yet building programs placed more up-to-date facilities at the disposal of
patients and doctors. St. Michael in Newark boasted an
elevator large enough to carry a bed in 1871—doctors and
nurses were accustomed elsewhere to carrying patients
from floor to floor by stretcher—and was described, in
1873, as a "bijou of a hospital, perfect in all its appoint-

* There is record of several abortive attempts at founding hospitals in this period. New Brunswick Hospital was chartered in
1872; St. Peter's, in the same city, opened in the same year but
lasted only until 1874; an Episcopalian Christ Church Hospital in
Elizabeth was chartered in 1873; and a Father Gervals was reported to be building a "Nicholas Moore Hospital" in Newark in
1871. It may be that some of these, like St. Peter's, did become
operative for a short time, but none remained in existence for
very long.

ments," and all of its 130 beds were said to be "constantly in use."

A delegation of the Medical Society of New Jersey visited the Massachusetts General Hospital in 1881 and found the "appointments worthy of Boston, but in some respects not quite equal to those of our new [but yet unopened] Camden hospital."

In the absence of medical schools, the New Jersey hospital of the late nineteenth century was essentially a place for medical and surgical treatment and care. It had not yet attained the status of a diagnostic or teaching center, except with regard to the training of nurses, although St. Michael's clinics, as we have seen, had made a beginning in this direction.

But even St. Michael had but two physicians in residence in 1904, according to a special report of the United States Census. Cooper Hospital in Camden also had only two, which was the typical number, and Mercer Hospital in Trenton had none. The Newark City Hospital had five, and the largest number of resident physicians, seven, was to be found in the Hospital for Women and Children in Newark. The visiting medical staff, however, might vary from 2 to 44 (the last at Mercer Hospital) with the 11 hospitals largest in admissions having an average of 13.

On June 1, 1904, only five hospitals in the State had more than one hundred patients. St. Michael was the largest with 276, followed by St. Francis of Jersey City with 260, St. Mary's of Hoboken with 238, Newark City Hospital with 215, and St. Francis of Trenton with 149. Cooper Hospital had 39, Atlantic City Hospital, 14; and Paterson General, 89; and these were perhaps more typical. For the whole year of 1904, St. Francis of Jersey City had the largest number of admissions, 3929; Newark City Hospital was next with 3752; and Jersey City Hospital third with 3011. Eight other hospitals had more than one thousand admissions during the year. The total number of patients in general hospitals in New Jersey on June 1, 1904, was 2284. This figure cannot be compared precisely with that given previously for 1890, but it does indicate that the hospital capacity and use had

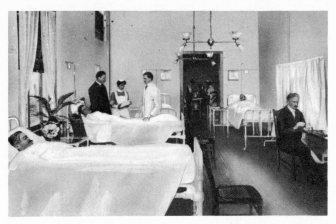
Men's Ward in the new wing of Mercer Hospital, Trenton, 1902

not changed very much. The fact that there were over 37,600 admissions to hospitals in the State for the year 1904 indicates, however, that the hospital was playing a very significant role in medicine and health.

It is impossible to evaluate and to determine just what portion of improving mortality rates can be credited to the hospitals. The availability of emergency service, the practice of asepsis and antisepsis in the operating and delivery roms, the provision of competent nursing care, all added their bit in the constant struggle against death and disease.

The growth in hospitals was not peculiar to New Jersey; it was a national development. The poor, for whom most of the New Jersey hospitals were first established, lost little time in taking advantage of the opportunities offered. The better-off also sought to take advantage of the existence of hospitals, especially in connection with surgery. Hospital care had begun to replace home care, and in the next century, as the number and size of hospitals increased, the hospital was not only to add new functions but was to become a much more generally used health facility.

The hospitals founded by Catholic orders had the immediate advantage of having a dedicated nursing corps at hand. The Episcopal hospitals similarly had available the services of the Sisters of St. Margaret and at the German Hospital in Newark there were Lutheran deaconesses who had had nursing training. The nonsectarian hospitals needed nurses, however, and when they could they brought in trained nurses from New York, Philadelphia, and New Haven training schools. But it was soon obvious that the only way to meet the demand was for the hospitals themselves to train nurses. Besides, it was also true that students would supply some nursing care cheaply since they would need only board and keep. Most important, however, was the realization that good nursing brought down mortality in the wards.

In 1882 both the Orange Memorial Hospital and the Paterson General Hospital began to plan for nurses' training. Which actually came first is difficult to say, but by July 2, 1882, Dr. Thomas W. Harvey, with the backing of the medical staff, had persuaded the Board of Governors of Orange Memorial Hospital to establish a training school. A Training School Association was founded, maintained by an active women's auxiliary, and soon the one supervising nurse had five students.

The school of nursing at the Paterson General Hospital also came into existence through the efforts of physicians, especially Drs. G. H. Balleray and C. Van Riper, two prominent gynecologists. The women of the community again provided considerable assistance, and in 1884, the school graduated the first two nurses. The School was fortunate enough to come under the supervision for its first three years of Mrs. Clara Weeks Shaw, who, while at Paterson, wrote *A Text-Book of Nursing* of about four hundred pages. The book was published in 1885 and at least three times thereafter, and was probably one of the earliest books written for nurses by a nurse.

Perhaps a glance at the curriculum of the Camden

Training School for Nurses at Cooper Hospital in the early 1890's will reveal something of the program involved. The trainees were given "didactic lectures" on medical nursing, surgical nursing, obstetrical nursing, anatomy and physiology, dietetics, and hygiene and general nursing. These lectures were supplemented by visitations, clinical demonstrations, and special instructions in general nursing care. There is no doubt that not all of the training was equally ambitious throughout the State, but we have no way to judge the quality of the product except by the occasional word of praise from medical men.

After this beginning, schools of nursing were added to hospital after hospital. Even the sectarian hospitals followed suit—Christ Hospital added a school under the Episcopal order of the Sisters of St. Margaret in 1890, and St. Joseph's Hospital in Paterson started a school in 1894.

The number of students grew along with the number of schools. The Newark City Hospital had 50 girls in training in 1887. Paterson General Hospital was graduating one to six a year, reached a high of 15 in 1898, and by 1900 had graduated 91 nurses. By 1904 a special census showed that 30 hospitals in the State provided training facilities for nurses.

HOSPITALS FOR THE INSANE

If New Jersey was somewhat laggard in the development of the general hospital, it was not quite so laggard in its development of special hospitals for the insane.

Dorothea Lynde Dix once referred to the State Hospital at Trenton as her "first-born child," for she felt a more intimate association with it than with the hospitals in Massachusetts and Rhode Island where the foundations had already been laid when she began her work there. Miss Dix wrought something of a miracle in New Jersey, but it has sometimes been forgotten than even in

New Jersey the groundwork had also been laid before her arrival.

Although New Jersey had provided for its blind and deaf in institutions in other states since 1821, in 1839 there was said to be not a single line on its statute books expressing sympathy "with those whom Heaven has visited with its severest inflictions." When Dr. Lyndon A. Smith broached the idea of a state asylum in his presidential address to the Medical Society of New Jersey in 1838, he was breaking new ground. The State Society took an official position in favor of an asylum in 1839; even before it did so a committee of the Legislative Council (Senate), headed by a physician, Dr. C. G. McChesney, had taken the same position. In the next two years a special State Commission and a joint legislative committee investigated and reported favorably. In New Jersey, they pointed out, the insane were confined to almshouses and jails, and in five jails, at least, the "lunatics" were kept in chains.

The arguments in favor of a State asylum were essentially three: the greater safety to the citizenry from the proper confinement of the insane; the basic humanitarianism of proper care; and, especially, the chances for recovery and rehabilitation made possible by modern medicine.

But 'despite impassioned argument—one report cried that "philanthropy bleeds and humanity shudders"—despite the benevolent activity of Governor William Pennington, despite the publicity given the reports, and despite a flurry of public petitions, the best that could be accomplished was legislative approval for a State asylum with the discouraging proviso "as soon as the finances of the State will warrant a sufficient appropriation."

Clearly, considerable spadework had been done when Dorothea Dix arrived in New Jersey in 1844. In January, 1845, she presented her famous memorial to the State Legislature. She had made good use of the reports just described, gave a vivid and detailed picture of the conditions she had found in a county-by-county visit to jails and poorhouses, lectured on the work of Philippe Pinel in France, and held forth the shining example of work with the insane elsewhere. Early in her memorial she remarked that New Jersey had "ample means, was unembarrassed by state debts, and prosperous in all her public relations, and more private channels of business." The State could not "fail to take an honorable and an honored position in the establishment of such state institutions," she insisted, and concluded with the cry, "Gentlemen, it is believed that the time has arrived for *action* upon the . . . resolutions. *'The finances of the state will warrant* a sufficient appropriation' for the establishment of a State Hospital for the Insane and Idiots of New Jersey."

But Miss Dix knew that reliance on memorials would not be enough. The legislature again had resorted to a joint committee which again (February, 1845) reported favorably. Three weeks earlier the Salem County poorhouse had burned down, and attention had been focused on the chained insane inmates, who had fortunately been rescued. Yet the legislature balked; some could not see spending so much money on a "few lunatics"; others thought the whole problem had been magnified beyond its true proportions. Miss Dix started her real work: "Early and late she was busy making interviews, overcoming objections, and winning over reluctant and timid legislators, and shaming cold and niggardly ones."

In what must have been a remarkable display of personal force, she finally garnered the support of the legislators. On March 26, 1845 the establishment of the New Jersey Lunatic Asylum at Trenton was provided for.

Dorothea Dix's work did not end, for she seems also to have been involved in the architectural plan of the building. Years later she was to return to the hospital; aged and ill, she spent her last days there in apartments provided for her by the trustees. She died there on July 17, 1887.

The hospital at Trenton was to incorporate some of the newest ideas in asylum construction. The building was roomy, airy, surrounded by gardens and "pleasure grounds." Altogether, the building sought to avoid giving the impression of a prison. Indeed the New Jersey State Hospital became the model for its time, a Massachusetts committee recommending it to that state in 1848, for example.

Such a building was essential to the new "moral" treatment of the insane. Kindliness and freedom were substituted for the imposition of restraints. Sympathy took the place of dislike and ridicule. Such attitudes, coupled with attempts to build up the physical stamina of the inmates, and determined efforts to keep them occupied with work, or games, or reading, would retrieve, it was felt, all that could be retrieved. One must wonder if even the training school for attendants in existence at the Essex County Asylum in 1890 could develop the intelligent, kindly, patient, and saintly attendants the list of duties promulgated in the early bylaws of the Trenton Hospital envisaged.

It was not long before the Trenton Hospital could not cope with the growing needs of the community. Only six years after the Hospital's founding, the Medical Society "earnestly" resolved that the "State should furnish such accommodations as will fully meet the wants" of the insane. In 1870 the Society went on record as favoring the establishment of a second asylum. While this was in the offing, however, two of the counties, finding that the State facilities were inadequate, built their own institutions. Essex County was the first, with the establishment in Newark of an asylum in a rented home. In 1884 a new building was erected, but not until 1897 did it move to Verona "to give the patients a chance for farm and garden work." There it was to take its present name of Essex County Overbrook Hospital, now said to be the largest county hospital in the country.

In 1873 the Hudson County Hospital was established, one followed in Camden in 1877, and Atlantic opened a hospital in 1895. Writing in 1890, a Trenton observer contended that, "The Essex County Asylum is certainly, in the main, a well managed institution, and a credit to the county and State; Hudson county asylum cannot be so well commended, and the plan and manner in which Camden county keeps its insane is a disgrace to all." Five other counties, Burlington, Cumberland, Gloucester, Salem, and Passaic, maintained insane asylums as part of their almshouses for the remainder of the century.

In 1871 the legislature provided for a second State Hospital at Morris Plains. It took its first patients in 1876—292 persons transferred from Trenton—and was acclaimed, even by outsiders, as "one of the finest institutions in the country, if not in the world." The New Jersey State Hospital at Greystone Park is now the largest of the four state-supported mental institutions.

The two hospitals grew in size and population in the nineteenth century but not without occasional voices being raised in criticism. Former resident physicians contended, for example, that the Trenton hospital had grown too large and was too crowded for the effective use of moral treatment and had fallen back upon routine practices and mechanical restraining devices.

Differences of opinion over the proper care of the insane had long been common, and New Jersey was obviously not an exception. It could not perhaps be otherwise when the causes and nature of insanity were matters of speculation and moralizing. Yet New Jersey did well for this group in the nineteenth century. In 1889 the State spent $222,380 on the state and county asylums, reportedly the largest sum expended for any single purpose. By 1900 the two state hospitals (Trenton for 53 years, Morris Plains for 25) had between them admitted 15,626 patients, of whom 7549 had "recovered" or "improved" and been discharged. On October 31, 1900, there were 2506 inmates in the state asylums, 1585 in the three large county hospitals, and 279 in the five other county asylums or almshouses. Altogether 4370 individuals were under care or treatment in a "public" facility.

A special United State Census report on the insane (1904) indicated that New Jersey had the greatest increase of all the North Atlantic States in the number of insane in hospitals per 100,000 of population on December 31, 1903, as compared with June 1, 1890. The ratio had been 120.7 to 100,000 population in 1890 and stood at 238.4 in 1903. Only Wisconsin and the District of Columbia showed higher rates of increase on a country-wide basis. Moreover, New Jersey's 1903 rate was the ninth highest in the country.

These figures might, of course, have indicated a high incidence of insanity in New Jersey. More likely they indicated, rather, that New Jersey, whose experience with insanity was really no different from the other eastern states, was in the forefront in the provision of hospital facilities. New Jersey had fulfilled the promise of Governor Pennington that it would not remain behind the other states "in the works of benevolence and charity."

VIII

THE NINETEENTH CENTURY—
RETROSPECT AND PROSPECT

In the last quarter of the nineteenth century, as we have seen, there came together in New Jersey fundamental advances in medical science and technique, new departures in surgery, the creation of a sanitary police, the establishment of hospitals and nursing, and a general improvement in living standards. Surely it would seem that this happy constellation should have augured well for the health and life of the people of the State.

Unfortunately, there are no adequate statistics for the incidence of disease in New Jersey in this period, but the State Board of Health collected and published comprehensive mortality statistics from 1879 on, and these give us some idea of the effectiveness of the advances of the last decades of the century.

The death rate in New Jersey haltingly, but generally, fell during the last 20 years of the century. A few bad years like 1882 and 1892 kept the rate high, but after 1892 there was a steady decline more like that which was to follow in the next century. New Jersey's experience was not unlike Massachusetts', the only other jurisdiction for which approximately comparable statistics are readily available. If anything, however, New Jersey seemed to be improving more rapidly as the century came to an end.

Where had gains been made? There was the virtual disappearance of smallpox as a cause of death, although it was later to break out again. Despite a rising population, the number of deaths in 1899-1900 from remittent (malarial) fever declined by 60 per cent, enteric and typhoid fever by over 35 per cent, scarlet fever by over 50 per cent, and diphtheria by over 30 per cent of the average for the two previous decades.

Some of the mortality curves indicated improvement. Tuberculosis showed an appreciable decline—despite its occasional ups— from a rate of 27.3 (1879) to 18.4 (1900) per 10,000 population. The rate for diphtheria, which had almost constantly moved upward from 1879 to 1888, and showed some slight signs of decline thereafter, really fell precipitously after 1896. In 1888 the mortality rate for diphtheria and croup stood at 14.8 (per 10,000 population); in 1900 it stood at 4.8. The malaria curve showed the most improvement. After reaching a high 3.7 (per 10,000 population) in 1881, it fell quite rapidly and regularly to 0.4 in 1900.

Some of these improvements can be accounted for. Obviously the disappearance of smallpox had been the result of the vaccination activities. Diphtheria's decline after 1896 probably reflected the increasing use of anti-toxin in New Jersey, after a rather guarded introduction of it the year before. Some contended, however, that the decline reflected only the new diagnostic techniques used by the new biological laboratories. These indicated that a great many cases that had once been diagnosed as diphtheria were not diphtheria. The decline in the mortality rates of other of the communicable diseases (tuberculosis, malaria, typhoid fever) reflected the improvements in sanitation, hygiene, diagnosis, and care.

But the picture in New Jersey in 1900 was not entirely bright. Behind the declining curves and rates there were large *numbers* of deaths and much larger numbers of non-fatal illnesses. Diphtheria was about to be defeated, but in 1900 there were still 927 deaths in the State from the disease. Typhoid fever, which had killed an average of 562 people a year in New Jersey for over two decades, had not been quite so devastating for the last four years of the century, but there were still 356 deaths from the disease in the State in 1900. If the experience of Cooper Hospital, where fatalities from typhoid fever from 1890 to 1899 averaged 5.32 per cent of the cases per year, and the experience of the City of Camden for the four and a half years from 1896 to 1900, where the rate was 10.3 per cent, were to be applied on a state-wide basis, it would mean that the average of 564 fatalities represented anywhere from 5475 to 10,620 cases per year in the State.

Moreover, some of the mortality curves were not moving in the right direction. Deaths from scarlet fever had gone down but had leveled off at about two hundred per year. Deaths from measles and whooping cough showed little of a long-term trend, although an upward movement (i.e., increase in incidence) was discernible. Worst of all was the cancer curve—in all probability reflecting better diagnosis and reporting rather than greater incidence of the disease. With only three years in which there was even a slight decline, its march was steeply upward from a rate of 3.7 (per 10,000 population) in 1879 to 4.8 in 1900. No fewer than 921 deaths were recorded as being due to cancer in 1900.

And finally, there were those diseases which showed little inclination to disappear with the century. The major causes of death were no longer the fevers and infections of the earlier part of the century. The five major causes of death in the State in 1900 were, in order of importance, "acute lung diseases," "consumption," "diarrhoeal diseases of children," "adult brain and spinal diseases," and "diseases of heart and circulation."

That the experience in New Jersey with health and disease was not better was to be expected in a state where industrialization, growth of population, and urbanization were taking place so rapidly. By 1900 the State had a total population of 1,883,669. There were 13 communities of over 20,000; Newark was close to a quarter of a million, Jersey City had passed the 200,000 mark, Paterson was over 100,000, Trenton and Camden were over 70,000 and Hoboken and Elizabeth were over 50,000.

Although the three biggest cities did not have the highest death rates,* and although some of the smaller communities showed up poorly,** the fact is that in 11 of the 13 largest communities in the State (the exceptions were Trenton and East Orange) the death rate was higher than the average for the entire State. Sanitary and humanitarian efforts notwithstanding, urban congestion and poverty showed grimly through the statistics.

All of this is not to say that New Jersey's health record was any worse than its neighbors. According to the United States Census of 1890 New Jersey showed a better record than its northeastern neighbors—New York, Connecticut, Rhode Island, and Massachusetts—in some diseases. New Jersey had the lowest death rate of the five states from the overall "general diseases," i.e., the main infectious diseases, and had moved up from fourth to first place in a decade. But for diphtheria and croup New Jersey had the poorest record of the five in both 1890 and 1900. Indeed there is nothing to indicate that New Jersey differed appreciably from its sister states in these matters.

The Prospect

The nineteenth century ended with some considerable accomplishment but much more promise. Professional, institutional, and governmental health facilities were available or becoming increasingly available, and scientific knowledge was painstakingly being accumulated. But looking back at the century, one must come away with the impression that medical progress in New Jersey was not only slow, but somewhat lagging behind the pace set by academic medicine elsewhere. This was probably just as true of other states as well, but the absence of medical schools in New Jersey, the scarcity of teaching

* Newark ranked tenth, Jersey City seventh, and Paterson twelfth among the communities of the State.
** Burlington (pop. 7392), Salem City (pop. 5811), and Gloucester City (pop. 6840) ranked first, eighth and ninth respectively.

X-ray apparatus at the Hospital for Crippled Children, Newark, 1900

clinics, and the lateness of hospital development imposed particular handicaps on the State. There are indications, too, of a general conservatism among the profession—too many practitioners of the last quarter of the century had been trained in a different age. To them the new language of bacteriology, immunology, and biochemistry was virtually unintelligible. Their reports and discussions too frequently showed that they still mistook observation for diagnosis, and trial-and-error dosing for therapy.

But many aids had become available to the physician. He did not have to understand the principles of immunity to use vaccines or, later, antitoxins. He had embraced asepsis and antisepsis even before he had accepted the germ theory of disease. Similarly, the sanitarian had called for hygiene before he knew exactly why it would work. But by the end of the century what had been done mainly because it had worked was beginning to be understood.

It was obvious that medicine had made great strides in the nineteenth century, but the explorations started and beachheads established were only a beginning. In medicine there was the discovery of the whole astounding world of micro-organisms and the pointing of directions for the conquest of that world by prevention and cure. In physiology the mysteries of the internal secretions had been looked into. In epidemiology the vector role of the insect was being revealed. In psychiatry the moral treatment had laid the groundwork for an objective and clinical approach to insanity. In surgery the scalpel had already probed into the innermost recesses of the human body. In diagnosis the X ray had literally given man a new vision. The nineteenth century had indeed taken man far in his search for health and long life, but these advances were to pale into undeserved insignificance in comparison with the waves of conquest they unleashed.

IX

MEDICAL ADVANCE
IN THE TWENTIETH CENTURY

IT IS OUR DEEP SEATED CONVICTION that we are on the threshold of the discovery of a cure not only for tuberculosis, but also for cancer," averred Dr. Norton L. Wilson in his presidential address before the Medical Society of New Jersey on June 10, 1913. He was of course much too sanguine, but his optimism points up the fact that the first third of the present century was one of constant and even rapid advance in medicine, a fact sometimes lost sight of in contrast to the rapidity of the advances in the second third of the century. True, the work of Robert Koch with a tuberculosis vaccine proved abortive, and the researches on cancer by Paul Ehrlich were to yield no immediate results, but medicine had begun to take its place as a science.

This process—the progress of medicine as a science— is indicated by an increasing awareness of the ramifications of the nature of disease and of etiological factors. By World War I, New Jersey physicians were aware of the role of the thyroid in Graves' disease and the role of the pancreas in diabetes, for example. To a knowledge of bacterial infection had been added a knowledge of protozoan infection. The vector role of the mosquito was not only well known, it was to lead to a very significant movement of mosquito eradication in the State, as will be described later.

But perhaps even more important in the development of medicine as a science was the availability of numerous diagnostic aids. The significance of systolic and diastolic blood pressure was known to New Jersey physicians at least as early as 1907, and the practitioner and especially the surgeon and anesthetist were being exhorted not to neglect the sphygmomanometer. In the same decade, to the qualitative analysis of the urine was added the analysis of the blood—and in an age when abdominal surgery continued its vogue, the blood count was a significant factor in staying the scalpel. Red cells, white cells, polymorphonuclears, lymphocytes, and eosinophiles were counted. Blood was being studied by spectrograph as well. Not only the urine and blood were subjected to tests: the feces, the sputum, the spinal fluid, and the stomach contents were also being examined, both microscopically and chemically. The various scopes came into general use, and the cystoscope and proctoscope (for the visual examination of the bladder and rectum respectively) were instruments frequently employed.

There were in use, moreover, a growing number of tests, both laboratory and physical, to aid the practitioner in his diagnosis. The Widal test and Ehrlich's diazo reaction for typhoid fever (even before the turn of the century), tuberculin tests, the Wassermann test for syphilis, Kernig's test for meningitis, and the Babinski reflex in neurological examination were all well known to the New Jersey physician before 1911.

But perhaps the greatest aid to precise diagnosis, particularly with regard to the infectious diseases, was bacteriological examination. In New Jersey this process was made easier by the availability of the Bacteriological Laboratory of the State Board of Health. In February, 1908, to illustrate how significant this became, the laboratory made 2773 examinations (of these 2336 were for suspected cases of diphtheria, 287 of tuberculosis, 135 of typhoid fever, seven of malaria, and eight miscellaneous).

With all of these advances had come commensurate advances in therapy and surgery. To the diphtheria antitoxin were added a tetanus antitoxin at the turn of the century and the Flexner vaccine for cerebro-spinal meningitis a little later. Most significant was the development of Ehrlich's "606" or salvarsan, the first effective and apparently safe cure for syphilis (1910). With it came the introduction of the concept of specific chemotherapy. Ehrlich's work, used almost immediately in New Jersey, soon met with general acclaim. Other drugs introduced in the period included adrenalin, said to have been named by the optimistic Dr. Norton L. Wilson when he visited the laboratory of Dr. Jôkichi Takamine in 1901, and aspirin, the answer to a long search for an analgesic. The gingerly introduction of aspirin into use in New Jersey hardly envisaged the tremendous popularity and general utility this synthetic chemical was to obtain. The use of silver nitrate in the prevention of blindness in infants was known in 1896, and the State Medical Society sought to encourage its use by legislation and other means.

The X ray continued as a diagnostic device and became a part of hospital equipment. The use of bismuth for the X ray of the stomach was reported to New Jersey physicians in 1912. The use of X ray in cancer therapy was recognized rather early, 1902, and a report on radium therapy was carried in the State Society's *Journal* in 1905.

Th intravenous injection of saline solutions seems to have been first used in desperation, but soon after by design, in 1907. Anesthetics were augmented by the approval in 1907 of novocaine by the American Medical Association Council on Pharmacy and the use of spinal anesthesia in 1912. Blood transfusion, first mentioned in New Jersey in the nineteenth century and occasionally in the early twentieth, had to await later developments before its safety and general utility made it a common procedure.

The dates given in the above account refer to New Jersey and should not be taken to mean the *first* date; rather they represent early dates for which there is some evidence. Similarly the account should not be taken as a complete record of the new ideas, knowledge, and techniques available and used by New Jersey physicians. Rather it must be taken as a sampling of the progress taking place in medicine in the first third of the century, and of the spread of this progress into New Jersey. The introduction of new techniques of diagnosis (blood chemistry, for example), and new therapeutic approaches (insulin and vitamins, for example), began to arrive so frequently and in such great profusion as to make it impossible to recount them all here.

There is also something beyond the above innovations to indicate that progress was taking place in the State. In 1904 the annual *Transactions* of the State Society became a monthly *Journal*. The change was much more significant than a simple indication of growth in size. The new *Journal* solicited original articles from outstanding physicians out-of-state as well as within the state; there were usually couched in more precise language, and indicated a greater awareness of scientific methodology than did the "Essays" which they displaced. Frequently these articles recorded not only the presentations before some medical group, but discussion which followed the presentation. Medical developments and events from Europe as well as the United States were presented in abstract. Altogether, a great deal of education for the practitioner was to be found in the *Journal*. As the editor of the *Journal* from 1941 to 1952, Dr. Henry A. Davidson, commented, the *Journal* was intended as a "practitioner's book." Its purpose was not the publication of the results of basic research; it sought to be of direct use to the practitioner rather than a "showcase" for brilliant research activities.

The reports from the county societies, which gave such a good picture of nineteenth-century practice, were now far too empirical and imprecise for extended presentation. This must serve to warn us again that the level of medical science reflected in the *Journal* was probably at a higher level than the medical art practiced by the general practitioner. "We fail to have recourse to the modern aids to diagnosis," Dr. Karl H. Goldstone of Jersey City told his New Jersey colleagues in 1909. "We Americans . . . rely entirely too much on the symptomatic method of treating disease. . . . The American practitioner, possessed of a keen foresight, inspects, percusses, auscultates, asks questions, turns these observations over in his mind and makes his diagnosis accordingly." The lag between invention and use was still in evidence, but as medical education was to improve, and as organs like the *Journal of the Medical Society of New Jersey* were to see continuing education as part of their function, the lag was to be lessened. It appears, for example, that it did not take as long for salvarsan to gain general acceptance in New Jersey as it had for diphtheria antitoxin.

The advance in medicine and health in the early twentieth century is perhaps best illustrated by what happened to the death rates in the first third of the century. By 1935 smallpox and malaria had virtually disappeared. The death rate from diphtheria was but 1.1 per 100,000 inhabitants; for the years 1885 through 1889, when it reached its highest point, the rate averaged 117.2. The death rate from typhoid fever was but 0.5 per 100,000; at its peak in the years from 1880 through 1884 it had averaged 50.7. The death rate from scarlet fever also stood at 0.5 per 100,000 in 1935; at its height in the years from 1880 through 1884 it had averaged 63.1. Even pulmonary tuberculosis showed a remarkable drop from the 259.3 average for its worst years, 1880 to 1884, to 44.8 in 1935. Comparisons between statistics of the 1880's with those of the 1930's, it must be noted, can hardly be accepted with an exactitude, since great differences in medical diagnosis and reporting, and statistical methods, existed, but the trends involved are certainly clear.

The story of tuberculosis in the State is worth particular attention, for the decline in its mortality, if not its incidence, came about at this time without the help of chemotherapy, vaccines, or antitoxins. Sanitation, education, and isolation proved effective within their limits.

The turn of the century saw an upsurge of national

concern with tuberculosis. The National Tuberculosis Association came into existence in 1904. In New Jersey the campaign against the disease began in earnest with a report by the State Charities Aid Association in 1901 which criticized the casting aside of consumptives into almshouses. In the next few years the combined efforts of this Association, the Medical Society, the State Sanitary Association, and the press procured favorable legislation, and finally the necessary appropriation (1904) for the establishment of a State Sanatorium. In 1907 New Jersey opened the facilities at Mt. Kipp (Glen Gardner).

In 1906 the New Jersey Association for the Relief and Prevention of Tuberculosis (later called the New Jersey Tuberculosis League) came into existence, and this group was to keep tuberculosis under continuous surveillance and carry on a wide and effective educational campaign. For one thing, this Association succeeded in getting enabling legislation that permitted the counties to establish tuberculosis sanataria. In the next decades public and private agencies worked together, and clinics, nursing services, local health and welfare agencies, and tuberculin testing, all had a part in warding off the ravages of the disease. Newark, in 1911, introduced open-air schools. The sanitary campaign also involved the imposition of detailed responsibility by law on the attending physician, the boards of health, and the patient. The last was given the "duty" of carrying with him and using a sputum flask, among other indignities.

In the late 1940's and early 1950's streptomycin, isoniazid, and similar anti-microbial drugs were introduced, and tuberculosis appeared at last about to be conquered. The raw statistics indicate that the New Jersey experience in the decline of mortality from tuberculosis in the first half of this century kept pace very closely with national developments. For the first three decades New Jersey seemed to be doing a little better than the nation, but since it cannot be certain that all the statistics were measuring the same things in the same way, there is really no basis for assuming any special superiority for New

Jersey. That there was no room for complacency is evident from the title of the annual report of the Tuberculosis League for 1954-1955: "The Garden State, a State With a Major Public Health Problem."

Whatever complacency the medical profession and sanitarians may have had was shattered by the influenza pandemic of 1918. The first civilian case of "Spanish Influenza" in New Jersey was reported by a Newark physician on September 25, 1918. "In less than 100 days, the disease was to kill 12,000 civilians in our state," went one report. Perhaps "the greatest medical holocaust in history," one-half million were killed in the United States and some twenty million killed throughout the world. Fortunately, the pandemic left quickly and New Jersey's death rate, which had reached 19.8 per 1000 population in 1918, the highest it had been in 26 years, fell in 1919 to a new low of 12.7.

THE CONTEMPORARY SCENE

The second third of the twentieth century, our own time, is particularly noted for its developments in chemotherapy, antibiotics, and chemical therapeutics. (Here the term chemotherapy is used in Ehrlich's sense as the use of chemical remedies which attack directly the pathologic organisms in the body, without doing unbearable harm to the host, e.g., salvarsan and sulfonamides; antibiotics refer to therapeutic agents derived originally at least from biologic sources, e.g., penicillin, streptomycin; and chemical therapy refers to synthetic chemicals that evoke a reaction in the body and have no known or intended connection with micro-organisms, e.g., tranquilizers, synthetic hormones, diuretics.)

Sulfanilamide, the forerunner of the sulfa drugs, was first announced in 1935, and the first case report of its use, and dangers, by a New Jersey doctor appeared in 1937. Penicillin, although not available for civilian use until after World War II, was called to the attention of the New Jersey profession in 1943, and in 1944 the *Journal* of the State Society carried a review of the pharmacology, dosage, and toxicology of the new remedy. Streptomycin, perhaps literally a product of New Jersey soil, was first isolated in 1944 and reported to the profession soon thereafter. In 1948 clinical reports of its use were carried in the *Journal*.

With the advent of these chemotherapeutic agents and the antibiotics, the infectious diseases, including pneumonia, which had been New Jersey's largest killer in this class in 1935, seemed well on the wane. By 1960 the only infectious diseases that ranked among the first twelve causes of death in New Jersey were those in the rubric, "Influenza, pneumonia and bronchitis." These totaled under two thousand deaths, while those for pneumonia alone had been over three thousand in 1914, and those for pneumonia and influenza had been over three thousand in 1935.

As overall death rates declined,* the age of the population went up, and consequently the incidence of the degenerative and neoplastic diseases increased. The last two decades have consequently been much concerned with the amelioration of the ills of the middle-aged and the "senior" citizen. Chemical therapy has come into its own in this connection, and drugs that are anti-coagulant, anti-arthritic, anti-metabolic, anti-hypertensive, diuretic, and sedative have taken on a new importance. In New Jersey, as elsewhere, this has led to a special interest in chronic diseases, and the aging of the population has brought with it special problems of medical care.

---

* The State's highest death rate (since 1879) of 19.5 per 1000 population was reached in the five years from 1890-1894. The decade, 1930-1939, found the rate at 10.7. In 1960 it was 9.7 per 1000.

X

PROFESSIONAL ADVANCE

T HE EDUCATIONAL FOUNDATIONS and professional requirements of the health professions—medicine, dentistry, osteopathy, pharmacy, nursing, and others—all of
necessity had to improve if only to keep up with the
scientific advances of the time. In the twentieth century
the preliminary educational requirements, the length of
the time devoted to study, the intensity and extensiveness
of the curricula, and the requirements of practical experience, all had to keep pace with these advances. The
absence until relatively recently of professional schools
except in pharmacy and nursing in the State meant, of
course, that these improvements would be recognizable
only through other channels. These were, first, the caliber, interests, and activities of the practitioners, and,
second, the changes taking place in the legal requirements for practice in the State.

MEDICINE

The attainments of New Jersey medical practitioners
are attested to in a number of ways. One was their increasing appearance in print, not only in the *Journal* of
the State Society, but on the national scene. It is of
some significance that at least 35 articles in the *Journal
of the American Medical Association,* in the first decade
of this century, were written by New Jersey physicians.

Moreover, the host of local medical societies that cropped up throughout the State, meeting usually for professional purposes and bringing into their own little province some of the great men of the profession, indicated professional growth. Thus the William Pierson Medical Library Association of Orange listed among its guest speakers Abraham Jacobi, Charles McBurney, and Simon Flexner. Thus, too, such associations as the Essex County Pathologic and Anatomic Society, founded in 1908 (and holding its first meetings in funeral parlors), gave evidence that there were among New Jersey physicians men of studious habits and dedicated inclinations. Started by 7 men, this group had 180 members ten years later and 230 in the mid-twenties.

By the same token, the mushrooming in more recent years of the number of societies given over to a single speciality reflects an improving professional status in the State. A complete list of such societies is not readily compiled, but one might mention the New Jersey Gastroenterological Society, "one of the first, if not the first [such] state society in the United States," founded in 1933, and, in something of a turn-about, the New Jersey Academy of General Practice, founded in 1948.

The development of societies as an index to professional growth in the State cannot omit the Academy of Medicine of New Jersey. Founded in 1911 as the Academy of Medicine of Northern New Jersey, it has been and remains an important center for professional life and activity in the State. It organized and maintains what was really the first medical library in the State of any permanence and signficance, although it was preceded by at least three other attempts at establishing medical libraries in the early twentieth century: the William Pierson Medical Library Association of Orange, the Medical Library Association of Newark, and the Trenton Medical Library Association. The Academy is today the center of a program of continuing education, and over the years has sponsored symposia on timely topics. It has published, since 1951, a *Bulletin* which, among other things, has put into permanent form the results of these symposia. (The Academy, located in Newark until 1959, now has its headquarters in Bloomfield.)

The advance of surgery in New Jersey, like the progress of medical research, was of course hampered by the absence of medical schools in the State. Yet the fruits of medical research elsewhere could readily be brought to New Jersey through the literature, and if the medical centers would not come to New Jersey, its surgeons could go to the medical centers. Thus Dr. Edward Zeh Hawkes of Newark managed to observe such noted figures as Moynihan (of England), Halsted (of Baltimore), Rodman (of Philadelphia), and the Mayos (of Rochester, Minn). Dr. Harry N. Commando of Newark took time off from his practice to study gastric surgery in Europe. Dr. Richard D. Swain went regularly, from 1932 to 1939, to Baltimore to study the neurosurgical methods of Walter

Operation at Mercer Hospital, Trenton, 1902

Dandy. Such men brought new procedures back to New Jersey and trained others in them.

A hurried view of the New Jersey literature might give the impression that virtually the only operations performed in the first decades of this century were on the uterus and ovaries or on the appendix. The last obviously became a common surgical venture: Dr. Edward W. Sprague and his surgical staff at the Presbyterian Hospital in Newark reported in 1938 on no less than 1463 consecutive cases of appendicitis. But surgery was much more "general," as witness the list of operations performed at St. Peter's Hospital in New Brunswick in 1910:

Amputation of tibia and fibula, 5; amputation of phalanges, 4; amputation of ulna and radius, 3; amputation of breast, 2; abdominal adhesions, 4; appendectomy, 102; abdominal abscess, 1; adenectomy, 18; colporrhapy, 4; curetting, 22; carcinoma, uterus, 4; carcinoma, bladder, 1; carcinoma, liver (ex.), 2; carcinoma, anodenum (ex.), 2; carcinoma, stomach (ex.), 4; coccigectomy, 1; cholecystotomy, 14; ectopic gestation, 3; empyema, 2; ectopic gestation, double, 1; fistula-in-ano, 2; facial cysts, 3; Gilliam operation, 27; gunshot wounds, 6; herniotomy, 19; hemorrhoids, 7; hysteropexy, 6; hysterectomy, 8; incision of abscesses, 7; lithotomy, 4; mastoid operation, 2; nephropexy, 13; nephrectomy, 3; ovarian cysts, 21; perineorraphy, 6; polypus, 3; prostatectomy, 2; prostatectomy, sup, 1; tub. glands removed, 5; trachelorrhaphy, 7; tenoplasty, 2; salpingotomy, 11; skin-grafting, 2; un-united fractures set, 3; ventro-fixation, 10; ventro-suspension, 13; vesico-vaginal fistula, 2; varocele, 1; intussuception, 2; wiring a patella, 1; tumors, 18; total 416.

Indeed, as New Jersey took up the results of accomplishments elsewhere, occasionaly adding a touch of her own, and as hospital facilities in general, anesthetics, the X ray, blood transfusion, and antiseptic and aseptic procedures and antibiotics kept improving (the rubber glove was reportedly intoduced into New Jersey by Dr. Hawkes after watching Dr. Halsted use it at Baltimore early in the century), there was virtually no kind of surgery that could not and was not performed in New Jersey.

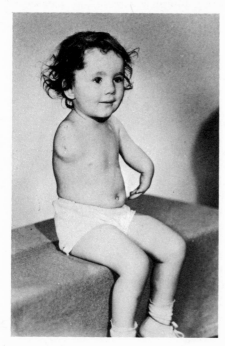

Cineplastic work at Kessler Institute for Rehabilitation, West Orange

Several advances in surgery in New Jersey deserve particular attention. Dr. Wells P. Eagleton, working in the field of cranial surgery, was the rare New Jerseyman to receive the acclaim that medicine and science grant in the eponym. The "Eagleton technic" became the basic procedure in the operation for petrositis, an infection of an area near the mastoid. Cineplastic surgery (by which the muscles are made to operate artificial limbs) became the special interest of Dr. Henry H. Kessler, who developed his own cineplastic operations in the 1930's. Finally there was the introduction of cardiovascular (heart and blood vessel) surgery at St. Michael Hospital in Newark. There had been a heart clinic at St. Michael since 1936. With the announcement of the pioneer work on heart surgery being done elsewhere, the men at St. Michael Clinic recognized the need for training cardiovascular surgeons. They took two signficant steps: first a cardiovascular surgery team, composed of Drs. Anthony D. Crecca, John J. McGuire, Joseph V. Crecca, and Lawrence Gilbert, developed their techniques in the animal laboratories; second, they invited two of the pioneers in the field, Dr. Charles P. Bailey (formerly a New Jerseyman) and Dr. Claude S. Beck, to train their staff. Since January, 1950, heart surgery has been performed at St. Michael.

Generally, New Jersey surgeons gained national and international acclaim for themselves by their work and contributions. Drs. Irvin E. Deibert of Camden, Edward W. Sprague of Newark, and John C. McCoy of Paterson were among the founding members of the American Board of Surgery (1937). Dr. Kipp, as noted earlier, was president of both the American Ophthalmological and the American Otological Societies. Dr. Wells P. Eagleton, who was referred to by his colleagues as New Jersey's "most distinguished physician" and who was president of both the American Otological Society and the American Academy of Ophthalmology (1924, 1934), gained international recognition for his work. Dr. F. Elmore Hubbard of Montclair was president of the American Society of Anesthetists (1940). Dr. Clarence R. O'Crowley was president of the American Urological Association (1925), and Dr. Lyndon A. Peer was president of both the Society of Plastic and Reconstructive Surgery (1942) and the American Association of Plastic Surgeons (1959). In addition, significant texts in surgery came from the pens of New Jersey practitioners: Dr. Wells P. Eagleton published the first of his works on *Brain Abscess* in 1922; Dr. Henry H. Kessler wrote on *Accidental Injuries* in 1931; Dr. George P. Pitkin issued a "monumental" book on *Conduction Anesthesia* in 1946; Dr. Toufik Nicola published his *Atlas of Surgical Approaches to Bones and Joints* in 1947; Dr. Meredith Campbell wrote a standard text on *Clinical Pediatric Urology* in 1951; and Dr. Peer published a treatise on *Transplantion of Tissues* in 1955. In the same vein, it needs to be noted that Dr. Max Danzis was acclaimed for his work on arterial embolectomy (surgical removal of embolisms) and in 1929 was invited to give the Hunterian Lecture before the Royal College of Surgeons in England. Dr. Kessler, who was Hunterian Lecturer six years later, received the Gold Medal of the American Academy of Orthopedics in 1936 for his work in cineplastics, among other honors.

The above account is intended merely to indicate that the role of New Jersey surgeons was an active one. New Jersey profited from the development of modern surgery but at the same time contributed to that development.

PROFESSIONAL LEGAL REQUIREMENTS

The system of licensing physicians in the State that was established in 1890 was subjected to review before too long. For one thing, although now the homeopaths and eclectics had not only achieved respectability, but were also being greeted by the allopaths as brethren, new onslaughts against the bastions of orthodox medicine were coming from osteopaths, chiropractors, and optometrists. For another, medical education in the country, especially

≈§ 127 §≈

after the Flexner Report of 1910, began to show considerable improvement, and the profession in New Jersey needed to bring its requirements for practice in line with these new standards.

That this was happening without planning is evident from the fact that, in 1903, 21 per cent of all candidates for licensure held academic or scientific degrees taken before medical training, as compared with 5 per cent "a few years" before. But nevertheless the possibility that New Jersey might become a dumping ground for the worst of the output of the marginal medical schools needed to be avoided. There was, moreover, some talk early in the century of overcrowding in the profession; high standards of education would help correct the situation.

Thus in 1903 the medical educational requirement for licensure was raised to four years of medical school; in 1915 a statute made one year of premedical education a requirement after July 1, 1919, and two years a requirement after July 1, 1920. Even more important was the requirement of a one-year internship after July 1, 1916. The Medical Society claimed only to have "assisted" in the passage of the statute, and its Committee on Legislation announced the passage of the Act with the comment that New Jersey was now "practically on a par" with New York. Perhaps like the 1915 statute, it was prepared under the direction of the State Board of Medical Examiners.

Although there were numerous changes in the legislation pertaining to medicine after 1915, the pattern of educational requirements and licensing established then is still basically in effect today.

Two State examining boards came into existence in New Jersey before the State Medical Board, those of dentistry and pharmacy. The Dental Board was created in 1873, was abolished from 1884 to 1890, and then was reestablished in the general pattern of the Medical Board. Since 1915 graduation from an approved dental school has been the basic requirement for licensure. Legislation pertaining to dentistry since then has been mainly devoted to the elimination of commercialized practices.

The State Board of Pharmacy was established in 1877 and is the one of these boards with the longest continuous history. The licensing of pharmacists also went through a slow process of increasing control and mounting requirements. By 1918 (effective in 1920) graduation from a college of pharmacy was required and in 1935 a one-year internship was required. Other legislation placed responsibilities on the pharmacist in the handling and dispensing of poisons, hypnotic drugs, and prescription drugs.

MEDICAL SECTARIANISM

The sectarian quarrels of the nineteenth century did not continue for very long into the twentieth century. Some of the old ideas of hydropathy and the use of electricity did become respectable enough to be absorbed by the orthodox practitioner into his therapy. Homeopathy and eclecticism had achieved so much respectability that in 1909 Dr. Wells P. Eagleton, the retiring president of the Medical Society of New Jersey, was suggesting at open meeting that the New Jersey Society go out "as an older brother, asking them to join us, and receiving any overtures that they may make as a compliment."

Partly this new attitude derived from the gradual change that had taken place in homeopathy as it became less doctrinaire. Partly it was due to the fact that the mixed representation of allopaths and homeopaths on the State Medical Board worked—in 1905 the Society was ready to acknowledge the cooperation and fairness of the homeopathic representatives on the Board. But certainly a significant force that brought allopaths and the homeopaths together was a new common enemy, the osteopath. As early as 1903 the two groups cooperated in opposing a bill to license osteopaths.

The struggle of the regular—now including homeopathic—practitioners against the osteopaths was a long one. The latter group had a background of a ninteenth-century cult with a monistic theory of disease and a system of therapy peculiar to itself. Osteopathy was defined in 1913, when finally legislation was passed, as "a method or system of healing whereby displaced structure [sic] of the body are replaced in such a manner by the hand or hands of the operator that the constituent elements of the diseased body may reassociate themselves for the cure of the disease." The medical men blasted this as a scheme for the improper practice of medicine nourished by the diploma mills, and a danger to the public health. A constant guerilla warfare continued until 1935, when legislation made it possible for the osteopath to add to his "osteopathic management," the practices and rights of the "regular" practitioner. Osteopaths who met certain prescribed educational or experience requirements could thenceforth take the regular medical examinations—including materia medica, therapeutics, and surgery—and if he qualified be licensed to "practice medicine and surgery."

Thereafter the major difficulty of the osteopathic practitioners was extra-legal, that of attaining hospital affiliation, usually denied on the grounds that the osteopathic physician was not a graduate of a medical college approved by the American Medical Association and not a member of the County Medical Society. Where there were enough osteopaths they consequently have organized their own hospitals. In New Jersey the Memorial General Hospital in Union and the Cherry Hill Hospital in Camden County are approved by the American Osteopathic Association. The latter is approved for the training of interns and for the training of nine residents in six specialties. Lately the courts have ordered the admission of osteopaths possessing the license to practice medicine and surgery into general hospitals when the osteopath has sought judicial relief. Those osteopaths who otherwise qualify but did not or could not take the regular medical examinations continued to practice the older brand of osteopathy, but, since 1935, under a broader definition that permits the handling "of any human disease" and prohibits their prescribing of drugs for internal use only, rather than all drugs.

During the early decades of the twentieth century still another group sought to attain legal recognition and the right to practice their system without interference from the medical profession. This group was the chiropractors, whose system of therapy was based, with a measure of mysticism thrown in, in 1920 at least, on the "subluxation" of the spinal column.* The chiropractors had a more difficult time of it than the osteopaths. Never permitted to administer drugs or perform surgical operations, chiropractic did not seem to gain wide acceptance in the State. By 1953 the number of registered practitioners stood at 183, although it rose to 400 the next year as a consequence of legislation. The 1960 Census indicated only 293 chiropractors in the State.

Pushed from side to side by pressures from opposing forces, New Jersey has in this slow, and perhaps blundering, way come up with a working system of control and licensure of the various groups who practice some phase or system of medicine. All of these groups, physicians and surgeons, osteopathic physicians and surgeons, osteopaths, chiropractors, and chiropodists ** are under the control of the one State Board of Medical Examiners. The Board now consists of nine Doctors of Medicine, one osteopath, one chiropractor, one chirodopist, and (recently added) one bioanalytic technician. The last two are "qualified" members, who vote only on matters pertaining to their specialty.

This may not be an arrangement enjoyed by any one of these groups, but it does at least have a rational basis in seeking to limit each discipline to its own field of

*The 1920 statute construed chiropractic to mean: "the study and application of a universal philosophy of biology, theology, theosophy, health, disease, death, the science of the cause of disease and the art of permitting the restoration of the triune relationships between all attributes necessary to normal composite forms. . . ."

** Since 1908 the chiropodists have been examined and licensed by the State Board of Medical Examiners.

specialization and training. If the public wishes to patronize a non-medical practitioner, that is its prerogative, but at least there is the intention of protecting the public from the arrogation unto themselves by practitioners of knowledge and techniques beyond and above their training, and at least the public will have some assurance of competence within this training.

Two other groups—in addition to the dentists and pharmacists—remained outside the embrace of the State Medical Board. One was the optometrists, who fought the medical profession during the early decades of the century at the same time as the osteopaths and chiropractors. The argument of the medical man against the optometrist was not, however, on theory or system, but on the competence of the optometrist to examine the eye; their doing so, it was claimed, constituted an illegal and dangerous practice of medicine. The struggle started in 1898, and every attempt by the optometrist to get enabling legislation was effectively blocked by the medical profession. Finally, in 1914 a State Board of Optometry was established. The Board remains in independent existence, and examines, licenses, and supervises that profession.

The other group that remained out of reach of the State Board of Medical Examiners was the nurses. In 1903 New Jersey was one of the first four states to provide for the registration of nurses. A statute in that year made it obligatory for nurses to obtain licenses from county clerks on presentation of the stipulated certification of training. In 1912 a State Board of Examiners of Nurses was created to examine and register nurses (therefore a "registered" nurse) and this remained the general pattern thereafter. The original requirement in 1915 of one year of high school and two years of training school had become by 1936 high school graduation and three years of training school. In 1947, the Board, now the New Jersey Board of Nursing, was empowered to license both "professional nurses" and "practical nurses" on the basis of different criteria.

XI

MEDICAL EDUCATION
AND RESEARCH

A MOST SIGNIFICANT EFFECT of the proximity of New York and Philadelphia upon the medical history of New Jersey was the failure to establish a medical or dental school within the State. That there were either antivivisection or antidissection laws in the State are myths, although these myths have had a long currency.

Two segments of the health profession did receive professional education in New Jersey: the nurses and the pharmacists.

NURSING EDUCATION

In 1904 there were 30 hospitals in the State providing training facilities for nurses; in 1961 there were 35 hospital schools of nursing. That there should be so little growth in quantity reflected simply a growth in quality. The increased educational requirements for registration that found their way into law under the sponsorship of the State Nurses Association and the authority of the Board of Examiners to approve schools, meant relatively fewer, but better schools. As early as 1905, 20 training schools had a three-year course in nursing, and as this became a general requirement, the requirement of prior high school training was added.

In the 1930's the Nurses Association became interested in the establishment of a university school of nursing in the State, but nothing came of it. In the late 1930's, both Rutgers and Seton Hall Universities provided selected courses for nurses, but no degree program was offered until 1940 when Seton Hall established a School of Nursing Education. Ten years later this became a separate School of Nursing. Fairleigh Dickinson University began offering an Associate in Arts degree for a two-year nursing program, and then two distinct Bachelor of Science programs. The Rutgers School of Nursing began as a Division of Nursing Education of the Newark College of Arts and Sciences in 1951 and finally evolved into an autonomous College in 1956. The Rutgers program has been granting an Associate in Science degree since 1952 and a Bachelor of Science degree since 1953.

In general the college programs include both liberal arts and professional care courses, and require practice in an affiliated hospital. The title "professional nurse" takes on added significance as a greater proportion of nurses come out of such baccalaurate programs.

PHARMACY

The only institution for the training of any of the health professions in New Jersey independent of a hospital was the New Jersey College of Pharmacy founded in Newark in 1892. In 1927 it became the first constituent college of Rutgers University outside of New Brunswick. Its two-year curriculum gave way in 1925 to a three-year program, both leading to the diploma of Graduate Pharmacist. In 1932 a four-year program was inaugurated with liberal arts courses added to a curriculum in pharmacy, pharmacology, chemistry, biology, botany, and physics, and such, and in 1936 the college gave its first Bachelor of Science degree. Students entering pharmacy since 1961 are required to take two years of prepharmacy courses preliminary to three years of professional and scientific work, so that the Bachelor of Science degree of the pharmacist will represent five years of education and training after 1966.

A University of the State of New Jersey was giving pharmacy degrees in 1910, as was the same institution under the name of the College of Jersey City in 1915. It was also offering a program in dentistry, approved by the State Board in June, 1916. This approval was withdrawn in August, 1917, apparently when the number of failures among its graduates who took the State Board examinations exceeded 30 per cent of those taking them, and the dental and pharmacy programs seem to have collapsed together.

MEDICINE AND DENTISTRY

After the abortive attempts to establish medical schools in Jersey City in the nineteenth and early twentieth centuries no further step in this direction was taken until after World War II. In 1942 plans to establish a medical college in Newark as a private, proprietary school resulted in the opening of an Essex Medical College in January, 1945. Beset by administrative and financial problems, and despite the appearance of the names of outstanding men on the roster of faculty, the college did not meet the requirements either of the State Board or the American Medical Association. Half a year after its opening it was declared to be "beyond saving" and it disappeared in 1946.

The Essex fiasco at least seems to have awakened interest in the establishment of a first-rate medical school in the State. In November, 1946, the Trustees of the Medical Society of New Jersey unanimously approved the establishment of a state-supported medical school under university auspices. Thus began the movement for a state-supported school with Drs. Stuart Z. Hawkes, Royal A. Schaaf, Henry B. Decker, and others at the spearhead. The Trustees of Rutgers were approached, the House of

Delegates of the State Society voiced its approval, and the interest of Governor Alfred E. Driscoll and of the legislature was aroused. In 1950 a committee appointed by the Governor the year before was absorbed into the New Jersey Medical College Commission that was established by joint resolution of the legislature.

The Commission was charged with the formulation of "a comprehensive plan for the creation, establishment and maintenance of a medical college in New Jersey," and its *Report,* dated March 5, 1951, was a masterful exposition of the need for a medical school. It pointed out that the trend in the supply of physicians in the State was running adversely; that New Jersey students were no longer being accepted in out-of-state medical schools as freely as formerly; that the opportunities for New Jersey doctors for continuation training were limited; that the nation-wide shortage of interns and residents was "sharply accentuated" in New Jersey (in 1950 there were only 258 residencies available in New Jersey as compared with the national average of 389 per state); that a system of regularized health services was impossible without a medical teaching center; and that medical research in the State was seriously handicapped by the absence of a medical school.

The report went on to recommend the establishment of a school, to be associated with Rutgers, The State University, with facilities for an entering class of 125 and with an attached hospital of 300 beds. It deemed New Brunswick the best location. A dental school was also recommended.

There are indications that the Commission had been informed by Seton Hall and Princeton universities that neither of them would be interested in having a medical school. Even the response at Rutgers was not entirely enthusiastic. In the next few years it was clear that some saw a medical school as a tremendous expense and felt that adequate support to maintain a first-rate school would not be forthcoming. Some felt that the medical school would absorb State funds that would otherwise go to already undernourished segments of the educational structure within and without the University. But the Commission's argument for the need of a medical school was convincing, and there were also those at the University very much in favor of a medical school. On January 25, 1952, the Trustees of the University endorsed the plan of the Commission and agreed to "accept the responsibility" for the school.

The Referendum of 1954

After a false start, the legislature finally provided, in September, 1954, for the establishment of a State medical-dental school and health center to be financed by a bond issue of twenty-five million dollars. The bond issue, however, was to be presented to the public for approval by referendum.

The proponents of the medical school worked feverishly, but despite the cooperation of medical, dental, pharmaceutical, veteran, educational, and other groups, the referendum was defeated by a vote of 718,020 to 565,878. Hudson County alone provided 93,000 of the 152,000 majority against the measure.

The *Newark Evening News* editorially explained the defeat on the basis of the uncertainty over operating costs, the fears of a new general tax, and the belief that the Seton Hall–Jersey City Medical Center affiliation, already in the offing, could meet the needs of the State for a medical school.

The last item really was double-barreled. There had been during all the study and negotiations those who wanted the medical school at Jersey City and those who wanted it at Newark. Attempts had been made by physicians and politicians in both cities to get the new medical center for themselves. Both cities contended that they had the hospital and clinical facilities already established and waiting. There were consequently those among the medical profession who were at best lukewarm to the establishment of the medical center at New Brunswick, and those who were unequivocally hostile.*

The other element involved the opposition that developed among Roman Catholics in the state. The Seton Hall College of Medicine and Dentistry was incorporated two months before the referendum, and the opposition may have been no more than a zealous attempt to protect one's own. There were, however, undertones of fundamental political and social issues. The Right Reverend Monsignor John J. McNulty, President of Seton Hall, applauded the defeat of the referendum and was quoted as commenting that "the greatest bulwark against subversion is private enterprise in education." That is to say, issues of public versus private sectarian education were also involved.

THE SETON HALL COLLEGE OF MEDICINE AND DENTISTRY

In any case, the proposal for a State medical school collapsed, but there did grow up at Jersey City the new Seton Hall College of Medicine and Dentistry—the first fully accredited school of medicine in New Jersey. Monsignor John L. McNulty was said to be proud that it would provide medical education "without recourse to tax funds," and it is worth noting that both the first hospital and the first medical school in the State were instituted under Roman Catholic auspices.

In May, 1955, enabling legislation paved the way for an affiliation between the new school and the Jersey City Medical Center and the first entering class arrived in September, 1956. In 1960 there were conferred 71 medical degrees; for the first time in almost three hundred years of history of the State, the Doctor of Medicine degree was conferred on the basis of a formal program of education, pursued at a bona fide, recognized school of medi-

---

* In Newark a committee of physicians under the chairmanship of Dr. Henry A. Brodkin was extremely active.

cine within the State. By 1963 Seton Hall had conferred 278 medical degrees.

The College of Dentistry, however, cannot lay claim to this distinction of priority. Its clinic, equipped with 108 dental chairs and units, would certainly amaze the students who were awarded their dental degrees from the College of Jersey City in 1916-1917. There were 36 dental graduates in the first Seton Hall class of 1960; by 1963 the total reached 139.

FAIRLEIGH DICKINSON SCHOOL OF DENTISTRY

At virtually the same time, Fairleigh Dickinson University established its School of Dentistry at Teaneck. It, too, thought of itself as "an example of private initiative." Like Seton Hall, its first class entered in 1956 and its first graduates received their degrees in 1960. By 1963 it had graduated 156 dentists.

THE RUTGERS SCHOOL OF MEDICINE

Seton Hall College of Medicine has been admitting approximately eighty students per year and graduating thirty-five per year. This was obviously an improvement in New Jersey's contribution to the education of its own citizens in medicine, but the basic arguments of the old Medical College Commission still obtained. It was still true that New Jersey was dependent upon other states for the training of its medical students. New Jersey needed more medical schools, and, in fact, so did the entire nation.

For such reasons the interest of Rutgers, The State University, in a medical school did not disappear with the defeat of the referendum. Members of the faculty, particularly the Bureau of Biological Research, began to press the matter in 1960. A proposal from this group to the Kellogg Foundation for the establishment of a "Graduate Program in Human Biology" which was to involve a two-year program of medical education was the first concrete step. Governor Robert Meyner became interested and called a special committee to consider the matter. This group gave its support to the request for a grant and to the whole project, going to the extent of recommending the prompt procuring of a dean for the projected school.

In June, 1961, the Kellogg Foundation awarded the State University a grant of $1,073,200 and later that year the State University appointed a dean of a projected two-year Rutgers Medical School of the State University. Subsequently further grants, from the Commonwealth Fund of New York for $400,000, from the Merck Company Foundation for $350,000, from the Avalon Foundation for $250,000, from John and Mary R. Markle and from the Roche Anniversary Foundation for $200,000 each, and from a good number of others, provided the new college with a financial basis on which to start. By February, 1964 such grants totaled well over three million dollars. The Medical Society of New Jersey has consistently indicated a benevolent interest in the new school; a faculty and staff is in the process of recruitment, building plans are underway, and the first class is expected to enter in 1966.

Thus New Jersey has only within the last decade begun to train its own physicians and dentists. There is little doubt that the State has much to gain from the professional schools that have been established, but there are shoals ahead. The Seton Hall College has been experiencing financial difficulties, and the Rutgers project will be requiring additional support as it goes along.

RESEARCH

Although it cannot be doubted that the absence of medical schools imposed a limitation on the progress of medical research in New Jersey, it is also true that considerable research was and is carried on and that some of it was of outstanding significance in the history of medicine and health.

One can find no better illustrations of the ultimate value of basic research than the history of research in New Jersey at the university level. The painstaking work of Dr. John B. Smith at the turn of the century at the Rutgers College of Agriculture as he laboriously studied the characteristics, life cycles, and habitat of various species of mosquito made possible the practical engineering that went a long way toward the elimination of that pest. It would indeed have taken a particularly sagacious observer watching Selman A. Waksman working, after World War I, on the microbiological population of the soil, or on sulfur oxidation by bacteria, or on microorganisms and soil fertility, or on the nature and formation of humus, to have prophesied that such studies would eventually lead to the isolation of streptomycin, neomycin, and other antibiotics.

Waksman, New Jersey's Nobel laureate in physiology and medicine (1952), was a graduate of Rutgers who became a researcher and teacher at his alma mater. He was neither a physician nor a teacher at a medical school.

The success of streptomycin, particularly with regard to tuberculosis, is well known. But neither the brilliance of the accomplishment nor the fame of the Institute of Microbiology of Rutgers, built by streptomycin royalties, should blind us to the fact that Waksman has published over four hundred scientific papers and is the author, alone or with others, of 18 books. His latest publication, in 1962, was the third volume of his work on *The Actinomycetes*. He has long labored in the microbiological jungles and were it not for his and his pupils' spectacular success, he and they would really be no different from the dedicated scholars who are constantly searching for new truths in the many sciences and technologies that have an impact on medicine and health.

Thus at Rutgers, now the State University, there have been studies over the years on bovine tuberculosis, vitamins in human diets, the biology of water, parasitology in disease, blood types, human nutrition, photodecomposition of pharmaceutical chemicals, and the building and operation of sewage disposal plants. Much of this was applied research, it is true, but the kind of applied research that seeks to find scientific answers to perplexities and in which the motivations derive from a combination of intellectual curiosity and social responsibility. All the projects just listed and many others not listed had a significant impact on medicine and health, it almost goes without saying.

Along with the Institute of Microbiology, which continues as a research center where scientists from all over the world study, learn, and teach, mention needs to be made of the Bureau of Biological Reseach at Rutgers. Since 1936 this Bureau, bringing together bacteriologists, botanists, physiologists, biochemists, and zoologists, has been investigating basic problems in biology, but not neglecting to examine the applications of their discoveries to medicine (and to agriculture and industry). Thus the study of the basic biology of protein nutrition in plants, animals, and man has resulted in studies of malnutrition, cancer, and surgical stress.

At Princeton University there are presently studies in such new scientific worlds as nuclear and radio chemistry. More specific interests of scholars at Princeton include the sound impulses of bats, the structure and function of amoeboid movements and enzymes, and bio-luminescents. From any one of these there may come data and insights significant to medicine and health. The study of the problem of organized enzyme functioning in the living cell, for example, is a project which is likely to lead to an understanding of such metabolic diseases and defects as phenylketonuria, mental deficiency from a biochemical lesion in amino acid metabolism; sickle cell anemia; megaloblastic anemia; and galactosemia, which makes milk toxic to infants.

No account of the research activities carried on in the State can neglect the fact that from 1914 to 1950 the

Rockefeller Institute for Medical Research maintained laboratories at Princeton. Begun as a Department of Animal Pathology, the laboratories were later extended to include plant pathology and general physiology.

The research activities and accomplishments of the Institute at Princeton were truly amazing for their quality and quantity and for the variety of trails that were blazed. The complete record will have to await the publication of the full story of the Institute, and only a few illustrations can be given here.

Much of the work at Princeton was basic research concerning itself with such problems as the crystallization of viruses, the chemistry of enzymes, or the cellular development of parasites. Some was directed, and with success, toward practical ends like the control of hog cholera, tobacco mosaic, and the Japanese beetle.

Underlying all of the work was the conviction that understanding disease processes of the animal kingdom, and later of the plant kingdom, would be of value to the understanding of human ills. The conviction was borne out. The work of Richard E. Shope with influenza virus in swine was soon to be helpful in the isolation of the virus of human influenza. Wendell M. Stanley's crystallization of the tobacco mosaic virus opened new vistas in virology. William Trager's work with the malaria parasite indicated that a nutritional factor might be involved in susceptibility to malaria. The knowledge of the chemistry of enzymes was opened up by the work of John H. Northrop. A host of noted scientists worked at the Rockefeller Institute at Princeton over the years and it is not at all surprising that two of them became Nobel laureates, Stanley and Northrop.

The development of a medical school and dental schools in the State has of course brought with it opportunities for research that were lacking before. The Fairleigh Dickinson School of Dentistry has created, with National Institutes of Health help, a modern dental research center in its own building, and plans an expanded program of research at Hackensack. At the Medical

School of Seton Hall research on life-saving techniques for victims of kidney failure, on the basic cause of muscular dystrophy, and on the molecular analysis of human blood for eventual synthesis, is now going on. On grants from the New Jersey Division of Chronic Illness Control, Seton Hall has also been studying arthritis and seeking diagnostic tests for cancer of the gastro-intestinal system. These are but illustrations, not only of the kind of work going on, but of some of the great potential in research carried on at a professional school level.

New Jersey pharmaceutical manufacturers have been engaged in a quite different kind of research of considerable significance. For the most part these manufacturers —and New Jersey houses about 10 per cent of the nation's drug firms—have not been engaged in basic research. Their role has been developmental. They have seldom made the major breakthroughs: insulin, penicillin, streptomycin, the corticosteroids, and others have come out of university or medical center research activities. But the synthesis, the purification, the devising of production processes, the standardization of the drugs, and the manipulation of molecules in seeking to create more satisfactory compounds of a drug, these abound in the records of the New Jersey companies. These, plus the experimental therapeutics by which drugs are tested first in the animal laboratory and then clinically on humans, are what the pharmaceutical houses accomplish so well. Needless to say they are important processes, vital to the health of the nation. It was undoubtedly considerations such as these that prompted Selman Waksman to say with regard to streptomycin, "the antibiotics that we isolated . . . would have remained bibliographic curiosities," had it not been for the aid and activity of Merck and Company.

The laboratories of these drug companies are substantial and expensive operations. The Squibb laboratories, at New Brunswick since 1915, added a one million dollar cancer research facility in 1959 and a new one and a half million dollar pharmaceutical research laboratory has just been completed. The Warner Lambert Pharmaceutical Company at Morris Plains has recently made a four and a half million dollar addition to its Research Institute and increased its interest in prescription drugs. Moreover, these laboratories attract top-rate scientists and maintain direct connections with the best in the scientific world. Merck and Company has had close association with five Nobel laureates, two of whom, with two other Nobel prizewinners, serve as advisors to the laboratories.

POSTSCRIPT

Most recently, the financial difficulties of the Seton Hall College of Medicine mentioned above have threatened to force that institution to close. A special committee appointed by Governor Richard Hughes has recommended, July 28, 1964, that, in addition to its responsibilities to the Rutgers Medical School, the State take over the ownership and operation of the Seton Hall College of Medicine.

XII

HOSPITALS, HOSPITALIZATION
AND MEDICAL CARE INSURANCE

Fourteen counties in New Jersey had hospitals by 1900, and the seven that did not were all rural. The last three counties in which hospitals were established were Warren (1923), Cape May (1950), and Hunterdon (1953). By 1932 there were 76 general hospitals in the State (18 more were to be established in the next 30 years). Some of these were municipal institutions, but for the most part they were voluntary hospitals started on the initiative and by the philanthropy of private groups, some secular, some religious. A decided impetus was given to the building and expansion of hospitals by the federal assistance program. Almost eighty-seven hundred beds have been added or provided for from 1947 to 1963, for example, under the Hill-Burton program.

There were in 1961 a total of 140 hospitals in the State on the list of hospitals published by the American Hospital Association. These included both general hospitals and special hospitals (psychiatry, tuberculosis, pediatrics), governmental (but nonfederal), and voluntary. These contained 51,281 beds and showed an average daily census of 43,096. The rate of occupancy of these beds is consistent with the regional figures, and it would appear that New Jersey had met its hospital needs in this respect. Indeed, although there are only 14 states in the country with fewer acceptable general hospital beds in relation to population than New Jersey, it has been calculated that New Jersey has filled 92.7 per cent of its needs in this respect. In long-term care beds in relation to its population over sixty-five years of age, however, New Jersey ranks fifteenth from the top among the states, but it has met only 62.9 per cent of its needs.

Some of the hospitals in New Jersey are rather small; Franklin Hospital in Sussex County has only 32 beds, for example, but most range between one and five hundred beds. The Jersey City Hospital was the largest in 1961 (excluding the county, State, and Veterans Administration hospitals), with 1033 beds, and only three other general hospitals in the State had over five hundred beds (Martland in Newark, United in Newark, Cooper in Camden). Only 42 hospitals in the State qualify for internship programs, and only 52 qualify for residency programs.

The growth in the size and usefulness of the hospital reflected a growing public confidence. As an editorial of the *Journal* of the State Medical Society put it, in 1910:

There is no doubt that a great change has taken place in the opinions of the people generally regarding hospitals during the last decade or two. They have ceased to be regarded as the last resort—and a dreaded one—for the care and treatment of the helpless and unfortunate poor classes of our communities. The well-conducted hospital is now held to be the best place for the care and treatment of the poor and rich alike and as offering better results in many cases than home treatment would give.

Care and treatment still remained the basic function of the hospital, although as we shall soon note, other functions were becoming increasingly important. One of the chief innovations of the twentieth century in patient care was the grouping of patients by diagnostic needs rather than by economic status—an innovation which Cooper Hospital has claimed for itself in the Philadelphia area. Another innovation in the 1950's— and this seems to have been picked up rather quickly and widely by New Jersey hospitals—was the development of intensive care units by which critically ill patients are placed under constant surveillance.

The new therapeutic devices introduced into the hospitals reflected the fact that bulk, complexity, and cost put them out of the reach and abilities of the individual practitioner. New Jersey hospitals of course kept pace with such innovations. Thus, for example, the Presbyterian Unit of the United Hospitals of Newark and Moun-

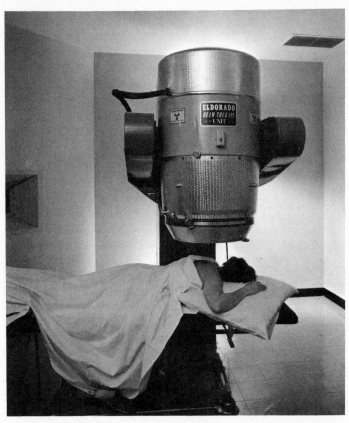

Cobalt therapy at Mountainside Hospital, Montclair, 1963

tainside Hospital of Montclair are equipped to use radioactive cobalt therapy. The Newark Beth Israel Hospital created a Radioisotope Department in the early 1950's, had radioactive gold available in 1953, and used radioactive iodine, phosphorus, and strontium before that. The West Jersey Hospital in Camden was also using radioisotopes in the 1950's. By the same token the great advances in surgery, particularly with regard to cardiovascular surgery, depended upon intricate hospital facilities and expert teamwork. The recent acquisition of an electronic and fully automatic heart machine and a special refrigerating apparatus at St. Peter's Hospital in New Brunswick is a good example.

It was not long, however, before care and treatment were relegated to only one part of the functions of a hospital. In addition, the hospital, even in New Jersey, perhaps especially in New Jersey, where there was no medical school, became also a diagnostic center, an educational institution, and a research institution.

A number of factors combined to make the hospital a diagnostic center. One was the cost, bulk, and complexity of equipment. The X ray, for example, was virtually impossible for the practitioner to install or use privately at first, and the introduction at Cooper Hospital, Camden, of a high-speed X-ray film-processing machine that delivers dry radiographs in six minutes is a recent illustration of the same situation. Another factor was the increasing availability in hospitals of the specialist and technician who could make the analyses and run the tests that were beyond the resources of the individual practitioner.

The role of the New Jersey hospital in education has already been noted with regard to the training of interns, residents, and nurses. But hospital staffs also use the hospital for continuing their own training. The Tumor Study Groups at Morristown Memorial Hospital and Englewood Hospital are cases in point, and in general, staff meetings, tissue committees, and special educational programs are all devices by which the hospital keeps the staff abreast of latest developments. Less well known is

"X-Omat," new high speed X-ray processor at Cooper Hospital, Camden, 1963

the venture of hospitals into the training of X-ray technicians at 13 hospitals in the State, and of medical technicians at 31 hospitals. An interesting educational venture is the publication of a *Journal* by the Newark Beth Israel Hospital. It presents the results of work performed at the hospital and provides the interns and residents

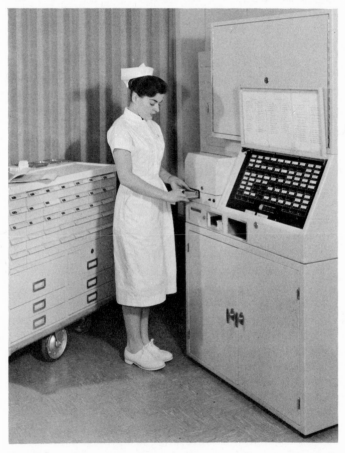

Automated drug dispensing equipment at Cooper Hospital, Camden, 1963

particularly with an opportunity to write and publish.

Research at New Jersey hospitals, despite the fact that because of its highly technical and often deceptively pica-yune character it gets really little notice in the press, is a constant on-going process. Clinical studies looking forward to the development of new drugs are not infrequently done, and such studies as "The Use of Fibrino-lytic Agents"—a study recently supported by the Essex County Heart Association at the Orange Hospital Center —is but one example of what goes on. The publications of New Jersey physicians are in essence reports of their research programs, for the most part carried out at hospitals.

Three accomplishments of modern medicine that were of tremendous significance and, as far as possible in the circumstances, original, have come out of New Jersey hospitals.

The first was the work of Dr. Harrison S. Martland at the hospital which now bears his name but which was at the time the Newark City Hospital. In 1925, when he was pathologist there, Dr. Martland became aware of the dangers of radioactivity. He traced bone sarcoma and aplastic anemia to radioactive mesothorium deposited in the bones of women who years earlier had painted luminous dials on watches. This was a primary contribution to the subject and when in 1926 he presented "epoch-making" historadiographs at a medical meeting in Newark, he was ushering in some of the grimmer aspects of the atomic age.

Second was the work of Dr. Henry H. Kessler in cine-plastic surgery and rehabilitation. After thirty years of experience in rehabilitation work as Assistant Medical Director and Director of the New Jersey Rehabilitation Commission (1919-1941) and for the United States Navy, Dr. Kessler's activity has centered, since 1949, at the Kessler Institute for Rehabilitation at West Orange.* This world-renowned institution brings both patients and

* New Jersey was one of the first states to create a Rehabilitation Commission in 1919.

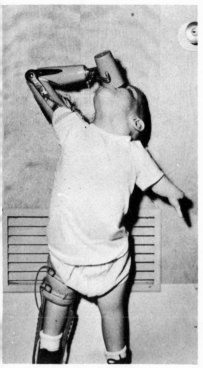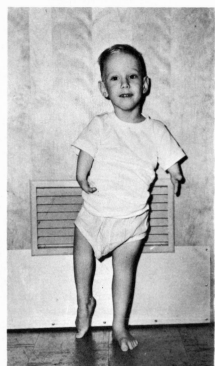

Cineplastic work at Kessler Institute for Rehabilitation, West Orange

doctors from the far reaches of the world—and Dr. Kessler has himself taken his skills to many parts of the world. The creation of self-motivated prosthetic devices and the process of rehabilitation from hopelessness and dejection to usefulness and determination, are miraculous monuments to skill, patience, and care—if one may mix miracles and human virtues.

The third was the work of Dr. Philip Levine at the Newark Beth Israel Hospital. Dr. Levine came to Newark in 1935 from the Rockefeller Institute where he had

worked with Dr. Karl Landsteiner and directly participated in the fundamental studies of human blood groups.
It was Dr. Levine's work that led to a knowledge of the
anti-Rh factor and its effect on the human fetus. His
postulation of an antibody that could cross the placenta,
immunize the mother, and then return to the fetal cells
and cause erythroblastosis fetalis (jaundice of the new-
born), opened up new directions for investigation that
eventually led to the saving of the lives of many mothers
and babies. Dr. Levine left Beth Israel Hospital in 1944
to become director of the Division of Immunohematology
of the Ortho Research Foundation. His contributions to
hematology are many and significant; the anti-Rh factor
is but one giant among many.

No account of hospitals in New Jersey can overlook
the Hunterdon Medical Center. The last county in the
State to organize a hospital, Hunterdon, when it finally
did open one in Flemington in 1953, created something
so vastly different from the usual small rural community
hospital, so bold in its planning, so broad in the scope of
its activities, as to make medical history.

In the first place, the hospital has become a health
center in a very wide sense. Its services go beyond diagnosis and therapy to prevention, rehabilitation, and education. For example, weight-control classes, prenatal
classes, multiple-screening diagnostic programs, and public health information are handled by or channeled
through the Center.

Secondly, there is what has been called "the most interesting, important and unique" feature of the Center,
the bringing in of a full-time staff of specialists at a rural
hospital and the development of a cooperative relationship between them and the practicing physicians of the
community. The family physician is in charge of his·
patient and has medical, pediatric, and obstetrical service
privileges. He refers his patient for diagnostic service and
for special consultation; major surgery is performed only
by the full-time specialist staff.

The specialists are primarily concerned with the supervision of the quality of the care given. They provide informal consultation and teaching, and seek to emulate university standards of medical care. All specialists charge for formal consultations and direct care, but their fees are pooled into a fund which is used to pay their salaries and fringe benefits. There has thus been a "mutual yielding of certain prerogatives by specialist and general practitioner" that has worked to give a very high quality of medical care to the patient.

Still a third distinctive feature is the affiliation of the Center with the Regional and Affiliated Plan of the New York University–Bellevue Medical Center. (Hunterdon is not the only New Jersey hospital affiliated with this Plan; Passaic General Hospital is another.) This has meant that all full-time staff members must be approved as faculty members by New York University. Each specialist devotes one day a week to teaching in New York, and the University keeps the work of the Center under continuous review through a representative sent to the monthly medical meetings there. The full-time specialists represent a teaching faculty that offers postgraduate education both formally and informally. Medical students, from the University of Pennsylvania, and the State University of New York, as well as New York University, spend elective or clerkship periods at the hospital.

Modern transportation and communication thus have altered both the image and the reality of the rural hospital.

The role of the hospital has clearly changed very much in New Jersey in the twentieth century. The Hunterdon Medical Centers are rare, but the hospital that one could "find duplicated in a 1,000 or more communities throughout our nation" can still pride itself, in the words of the Administrator of the Bridgeton Hospital, in "meeting the health requirements of [the] community with a high degree of acceptance and satisfaction on the part of the public."

Public reliance upon and the growth of the hospital in the United States was suddenly brought up short by the Great Depression. Hospitalization became a luxury only to be indulged in for a dire emergency. Many patients could not pay, and hospitals found endowment resources diminishing and philanthropic sources drying up.

Out of this came prepaid hospitalization as a device to protect the economic foundations of the hospitals. Tried by single hospitals here and there in the country, prepaid hospitalization found its first successful application for a group of hospitals in Essex County in New Jersey. It was in 1932 that the Hospital Council of Essex County began to explore the possibilities of using a prepaid plan as a means of easing the economic strain on the hospitals and of providing a fuller utilization of their facilities. The plan—with 17 participating hospitals—enrolled its first subscriber (at $10 a year, covering 21 days of hospitalization) in 1933. The next year the plan was extended to hospitals beyond Essex County. In 1936 it became known as the Hospital Service Plan of New Jersey and soon developed into a state-wide organization with offices in Newark, Trenton, and Camden.

The growth of the Plan in terms both of the services it offered and the numbers of individuals it has served, is no less than phenomenal. In 1935 it offered family coverage to dependents, the first plan in the country to do so; in 1938 it offered maternity-benefit coverage; in 1940 outpatient care was provided for; in 1950 benefit days for hospital care were extended from 21 to 120; in 1960 enrollment was open to persons over sixty-five years of age; in 1962 the "senior citizen" program was broadened. The number of enrollees reached one million in 1947 and two and a half millions in 1962.

Obviously here was a great change in American and in New Jersey life and health. Hospital services were now available not only to indigent charity patients but to the middle-income groups as well. In New Jersey about 40 per cent of the State's population (as compared with a national average of 31 per cent) is enrolled in Blue Cross. How really significant the plan is in the care of the sick is indicated by the fact that from its founding to 1962 the plan has paid $476,000,000 to hospitals, representing over four million hospital admissions. The Plan is paying benefits now at the rate of $80,000,000 annually and has become the fifth largest in the country.

In 1942 the Hospital Service Plan, known popularly as Blue Cross, was joined by a sister plan, the Medical-Surgical Plan of New Jersey, known popularly as Blue Shield. Although two separate organizations, their complementary activities, and the fact that Blue Cross is the sales agency and performs certain administrative functions for Blue Shield, have led the public to think of them, erroneously, as the same organization.

The Medical-Surgical Plan in some measure was also the child of the Great Depression, but in a different way. In the 1930's the great number of medically indigent had led to the development of a program of medical help paid for through the Emergency Relief Administration and operated through the Medical Society of New Jersey. The plan had provided medical service for those in need and income for physicians, without disturbing the pattern of what the profession considered proper patient-physician relationships.

But the depression scheme had suggested to some the possibilities of the government's assumption of a progressively increasing role in the provision of medical care. To many in the profession this would be, or at least would lead to, socialized medicine. To head this off the profession searched for schemes that would obviate the necessity for government involvement and yet provide needed medical services within a framework of traditional medical ethics and economics. If the profession failed to find such a scheme, government on both the national and state levels might be forced to step into the picture by the pressure of the medical needs of the public.

The scheme hit upon was that of a prepayment plan based on insurance principles. When the American Medical Association, after some uncertainty, finally gave its approval to such arrangements in 1938, the way was open for the establishment of medical-surgical prepayment plans.

Such was the background and the reasoning behind the Medical Surgical Plan in New Jersey. The man who took the initiative in this matter in the State was Dr. Edward W. Sprague. Within days of the American Medical Association action he convinced President W. J. Carrington of the State Medical Society of the value of such a plan, and a committee was appointed to study it. After some false starts there evolved the Medical-Surgical Plan of New Jersey; it began operation, with the Hospital Service Plan as its sales agent, in 1942. The Medical-Surgical Plan is controlled by a Board of Trustees, a majority of whom must be members of the Medical Society of New Jersey, and the nominations to which must be approved by that Society. Although not specifically named in this connection, it is the only group that meets the criteria established. In this way there is maintained a close and virtually controlling relationship between the Society and the Plan.

After a very slow start the Medical-Surgical Plan took hold. In 1942 it paid out only $5000 in claims; in 1962 it paid out $37,750,000. Accepted rather generally by the medical profession—in 1962 over 80 per cent of the physicians in the State participated and in some counties almost every eligible physician, osteopathic physician, and chiropodist participated—Blue Shield grew rapidly. In its entire existence from 1942 to 1962 inclusive it paid out a total of almost $150,000,000. In 1962 it moved from seventh to sixth largest such Plan in the country and in 1963 it moved to fifth place with an enrollment of almost 2,372,000. Over 37 per cent of New Jersey residents are covered by the plan as compared with a national average of 27 per cent.

It is thus clear that the Hospital Service Plan and the Medical-Surgical Plan have contributed to the health and well-being of the people of the State in a way that has had the acquiescence if not approbation of the medical profession. Yet the tremendous growth of the coverage and the claims paid do not in themselves mean that all problems have been met or that other problems have not arisen. One effect of the Hospital Plan has been the adverse influence on philanthropic support for hospitals. This in turn has complicated the problem of care of the indigent and of paying for capital improvements: often these costs have had to be passed on to the Plan members. Constantly increasing premium rates which result from these conditions, from the costliness of new techniques and instruments, from the over-utilization of the hospital, and from the general inflationary tendencies of the whole economy may limit the continued growth of the Plans, and price a large segment of the population out of the market. The "over-utilization" of the hospitals and even of physicians' services has led to cries for more disciplined use of such services—by patient, hospital, and physician—and hospitals like the Perth Amboy General and the Passaic General have instituted a formal program of medical staff control of admissions and length of stay.

The provision of the statute relative to medical-surgical plans by which the trustees of such plans must be approved by, in effect, the Medical Society of New Jersey has discouraged the establishment in New Jersey of rival plans. This provision has, however, recently been declared unconstitutional by the State Supreme Court, as part of the attempt of an organization called Group Health Insurance (GHI) to begin operation in the State. Should this Group finally succeed—and on July 15, 1964, the Supreme Court of New Jersey struck down the 51 per cent physician-participation requirement, thus removing another barrier to the establishment of GHI programs in the State—its plan expects to offer virtually complete medical and surgical coverage on a prepaid basis. This coverage will include office calls, house visits, annual check-ups, diagnostic procedures, and such, as well as hospital and surgical care. GHI still intends to give the patient and doctor a freedom of choice, but the participating physician would be required to accept the fee established by the GHI, whereas the Medical-Surgical Plan permits the charging of fees above the Plan scale when family income goes beyond $7500 per annum. This phase of the GHI plan is perhaps the chief bone of contention: there are those who believe the GHI scheme is destructive to the traditional freedom of the physician to establish his own fees.

The effect of opening up the State to one or more rival organizations to the Medical-Surgical Plan may indeed greatly affect the basic patterns of medical practice in the State.

XIII

PUBLIC HEALTH AND WELFARE

THE CHIEF GUARDIANS of the health of the citizens of New Jersey continue to be the State and local boards of health. The powers of these bodies remained essentially unchanged except that a constant stream of new functions fell their way. As the population increased, as industrialization expanded, and as science advanced there was more and more for them to do. Late in the nineteenth and early in the twentieth century, to illustrate, the boards became involved in such activities as milk control, prevention of water pollution, sewage disposal, the dissemination of diphtheria vaccine, and the bacteriological testing of sputum.

The first significant change in the administrative organization of the State Board came in 1908. In that year a new businessman board divided its work into five divisions: the Division of Vital Statistics, the Division of Medical and Sanitary Inspection, the Division of Food and Drugs, the Division of Creameries and Dairies, and the Division of Sewerage and Water Supplies. The last represented a new delegation of authority, the Board being given the powers of a former State Sewerage Commission.

In the next few years both the State and local boards were, however, subjected to considerable criticism. In 1913, for example, the Committee to Consider the Health Laws of the State, of the State Medical Society, recommended, in considerable detail, a thorough review of the

State law. In Newark, in the same year, the Essex County Medical Society criticized the Newark Board of Health for its failure to do anything about river pollution and for the inadequacy of dairy inspection.

In addition, the division of authority between State and local agencies was never properly spelled out, and perhaps the greatest problem of the State Board was getting the cooperation of the local boards. In 1908, 125 out of 460 of the local boards failed to turn in their annual reports as required by law. A serious attempt was made to remedy the situation in 1915. A "Department of Health" was created governed by a board whose eight members were to include three physicians, two sanitary engineers, and a veterinarian. The Department was empowered to promulgate a sanitary code for the State that would supersede local ordinances and which local authorities were obliged to enforce. The local boards were to be subject to the supervision of the Department, albeit the local agencies retained a great deal of their original power under a statute of 1887.

Complicated by home-rule issues, politics, and the stark fact that physical, ecological, and even social conditions do not respect political boundaries between municipalities and counties, the 1915 arrangements did not really provide satisfactory solutions to the problems involved. Various administrative devices to overcome the difficulties have been tried. A recent study has shown that the situation is not yet a satisfactory one, and further changes and experimentation will be necessary.

To return to the State Board, in 1947 the Department again was reorganized and the unwieldy rule-by-board eliminated. A Commissioner of Health was provided for and designated Chief Administrative Officer of the Department, and in 1954 a "Public Health Council" replaced the old Board. In 1948-1949 the Commissioner, with legislative authorization, reorganized the Department into six major divisions: Constructive Health, Environmental Sanitation, Laboratories, Local Health Services, Preventable Diseases, and Vital Statistics and Administration.

It is probably true that jurisdictional and administrative problems have limited the effectiveness of health work in the State. The role of the State Board of Health is, however, a very vital one, even though it comes to the public attention only when critical problems like the recent virus encephalitis endemic arise. Indeed, the public awareness of the work of the boards of health is mainly in terms of the control of communicable disease. The public is but subconsciously, if at all, aware of the constant surveillance and inspection that goes on to provide sanitation, of the struggle against water and air pollution, of insect-control measures, and of the laboratory analyses of increasing scope. Just as the prototype of the Department proved its mettle by educating the people in advance of a cholera attack in 1867, so the present Department has done similar chores with regard to encephalitis, salmonellosis, and viral hepatitis. Such educational activity is well known to the public; less well known is the regular stream of newsletters and the publication of the *Public Health News* that passes along current happenings and advice, with the necessary dispatch, to physicians, nurses, pharmacists, health officers, and others on the health team.

The State Department and the local boards of health will have to assume still greater responsibility as we move into the atomic age; administrative problems still need to be solved, expanding functions will require increasing expenditures, and both will require the development of "a sense of urgency for public health needs" among the public.

SEWAGE AND WATER SUPPLY

The turn of the century, as we have seen, marked a period of considerable innovation and progress in the science of medicine and surgery. So, too, did engineering in this period begin to solve the problems of waste disposal and water contamination.

The engineering advances, however, required the development or organizational arrangements without which progress would have been extremely difficult. Nineteenth-century legislation that gave boards of health and groups of private citizens some responsibility over sewerage systems without commensurate authority had proved ineffective. In 1899 the first significant step was taken with the creation of a State Sewerage Commission and the provision for the establishment of Sewerage Districts. In addition to comprehensive investigating powers the Commission was given authority to approve the creation of the Sewerage Districts, and no new sewer could be built in the State without its consent. The powers of this Commission were handed over to the State Board of Health in 1908.

In 1902 the Passaic Valley Sewerage Commission was created, and in 1903 was given power to build a sewer to service the 20 communities in its district. All other sewers in the area, public or private, were to be required to connect into it, and the sewage was to be carried out into New York Bay. Litigation held up the process, and actual construction of a trunk sewer was not begun until 1912. In 1924 it was completed, finally to bring some semblance of sanitation and propriety to the handling of wastes in North Jersey.

Other such agencies have been created. In 1917 "Joint Meetings" of municipalities were authorized to build and control sewers. In 1933 the Hackensack Sewerage Authority was created, and a Rahway River Sewerage Authority was established following the passage of enabling legislation in 1946.

The improvement of water supplies went through a similar development and was a concomitant of this improvement in public sewerage systems. Attempts at controlling pollution started in the nineteenth century (in 1884 the drainage of "sludge acid" into streams was prohibited by State statute), but effective control needed constant policing. This was the contribution of the State Board of Health. Regularly it inspected and analyzed water supplies, both public and private; regularly it looked for, reported, and prosecuted pollution. Indeed, although the pollution of waterways has hardly disappeared, the problem soon became not one of purity of water, but of the quantity of water. The Water Supply Commission set up in the State in 1907—when a court decision led to the replacement of many private water companies by public agencies—was more concerned with watersheds and water sources than with bacterial counts and pollutions. In 1929 a Water Policy Commission replaced the Water Supply Commission, and since 1948 a Water Policy and Supply Council, in the Department of Conservation, has had the responsibility. Be it noted that the provision of palatable water in sufficient quantity is also a health problem and not simply a matter of convenience.

The best measure of the success of these activities is of course the declining incidence of water-borne diseases. The Department of Health, however, maintains a constant surveillance not only of drinking water, but of fishing grounds and bathing facilities as well.

The Extermination of the Mosquito

Early in the twentieth century New Jersey earned for itself the sobriquet of the "Mosquito State," and outsiders spoke of the "Jersey Mosquito" as if it were an espeçially large and voracious species *sui generis*. The mosquito is to be found throughout the United States and there were other states with similar problems, it is true, but the tidal marshes of the Hackensack Valley and Newark Bay, the coastal marshes all the way to Cape May, and many upland areas bred and released enormous hordes of mosquitoes. It is true also that except for a short stretch on the Arthur Kill where Staten Island insects might invade, New Jersey's mosquitoes were all home-grown. Reports had it that the migrating broods of mosquitoes sometimes forced business establishments in Newark to close down, and attacking hordes of mosquitoes cleared the shore resorts of their guests.

The small and delicate creature was torture to the humans upon whom he fed, but harm came not from the sting alone: the mosquito as a vector was essential to the life cycles of the deadly micro-organisms that it transported to humans.

Benjamin Rush in 1790 considered the possibility that fevers were carried by insects from the marshes, but unfortunately for posterity did not—perhaps could not in the given state of science—carry through with the idea. The idea was not original with Rush—the role of insects as carriers of disease had been suspected since antiquity. But it was really not until 1879 that it received its first scientific verification. In that year the British physician Patrick Manson demonstrated that the mosquito was responsible for the transfer of worms that caused the tropical disease known as filariasis. Such studies were continued in Italy, India, and the United States and all added to the knowledge of the vector role of insects. They came to a dramatic climax in the well-known work with yellow fever in Cuba in 1899-1901. (New Jersey had its own martyr in this struggle in the person of Clara Maass, Newark nurse who had trained at the German Hospital. Nurse Maass succumbed to yellow fever in Cuba at the age of twenty-five, after she had volunteered to be bitten by infected mosquitoes.)

All of these exciting developments did not go unnoticed in New Jersey. A campaign to eliminate the mosquito was mounted at the very beginning of the century, bringing together the State entomologist working at the Agricultural Experiment Station, the State Board of Health, the State Medical Society, the State Sanitary Association, the New Jersey Mosquito Extermination Association (after 1913), and private individuals, all urging war against the mosquito.

The man who took the initiative was Dr. John B. Smith, State entomologist at the New Jersey Agricultural Experiment Station. His interest in the mosquito had begun even before 1900, and in 1904, with the benefit of a State appropriation, he issued his remarkable *Report of the New Jersey State Agricultural Experiment Station Upon the Mosquitoes Occurring Within the State, their Habits, Life History, &c.* This profusely illustrated volume of 482 pages not only described the characteristics and habits of the mosquito in general, but specifically classified and minutely described each of the species found in New Jersey. Dr. Smith discussed the problems of eradication at each locale in the State where there were breeding grounds, and described both what had been done and what should be done.

Dr. Smith sought help wherever he could get it. One after the other he got the attention and support of the Newark Board of Health, a conference of members of various boards of health in the Newark area, the Medical Society of New Jersey, and the New Jersey Sanitary Association. Civic-minded groups in South Orange and Elizabeth undertook mosquito control paid for by private contributions and the municipal governments of both Newark and Elizabeth soon began to appropriate sums for the drainage of meadowland.

This activity, and the publication of Dr. Smith's report in 1904 awakened the active interest of the State legislature. The pattern of legislation that emerged, and that was continued until 1956, made the State Agricultural Experiment Station the central and coordinating body, although not always technically the controlling body. The financing of the program was not, however, easily managed. Grants-in-aid by the State to the localities of one-fourth of costs went virtually untaken for 1905-1906, and even when the State provided for direct action under the Director of the Agricultural Experiment Station and authorized an expenditure over several years of $350,000, the money was not appropriated in anywhere near the amounts expected.

The Agricultural Experiment Station did manage, though, with the "noble" participation of Newark, Jersey City, and Elizabeth, all of whom footed nearly all of the bill themselves, to do considerable work in the marsh areas. Thousands of acres of meadowland were treated and millions of feet of drainage ditches were dug. New Jersey was said to stand "first in mosquito warfare" among the states in 1911.

In 1912 there were inaugurated County Mosquito Extermination Commissions whose funds, with prior approval of the Director of the Experiment Station, who remained coordinator of the program, were to be raised by taxes. The County system seemed to work. By 1919, 120,000 acres of salt marsh had been "rendered reasonably free from mosquito breeding"; over 18 million linear feet of ditches had been dug and dikes, sluices, and tide gates had been erected. At least 60 per cent of the upland pools had also been eliminated, and a system of patrol of mosquito breeding areas was in effect.

There seemed, in general, to be satisfaction with these procedures—of oil treatment and of drainage—for they continued to be used. A New Jersey Larvicide was developed at the Experiment Station and the hordes of mosquitoes effectively reduced.

Indeed, New Jersey seemed to have become overconfident. During World War II, shortages in manpower and materials, followed by rapid postwar expansion without proportionate budget increase for mosquito work, left drainage systems, dikes, and such deteriorating. Hurricanes in the middle 1950's aggravated the situation, and the State was again plagued with large hordes of mosquitoes.

Things became bad enough for the legislature to take notice, and on the recommendation of a Mosquito Control Study Commission created in 1955, the direction and supervision of mosquito control was placed in the hands of a new State Mosquito Control Commission with which the Agricultural Experiment Station (whose director was ex-officio a member of the Commission) was instructed to cooperate. Little change in the activity of the Station seemed to be contemplated but the ultimate authority was now vested in the Commission.

Again complacency was shaken by the outbreak of disease, this time eastern encephalitis in 1959-1960. This was a reminder that the mosquito was a disease carrier and not merely a pest, for it was strongly suspected that the *culiseta melanura* was the vector. A special emergency onslaught against the breeding places of this species in Ocean and Burlington counties was launched. To the older techniques of swamp clearance and drainage, was added the use of DDT and other insecticides.

Altogether the malaria statistics and the comfort of New Jerseymen with long enough memories to appreciate the difference in the buzzing and biting about them, demonstrate how much has been accomplished. The encephalitis affair reminds us, though, that extreme vigilance is the price of health, also.

THE SICK-POOR

The one facet of the history of medicine and health in New Jersey that seemed not to be taken firmly in hand until very recently was the provision of medical and hospital care for the indigent and the medically indigent.

Traditionally municipalities had taken care of their own poor in New Jersey and there are records of doctor's fees being paid by local authorities back in the eighteenth century. We have already noted the existence of hospital facilities of a sort associated with almshouses and the existence of free clinics and city dispensaries in the nineteenth century. We have noted, too, that hospitals were originally charity institutions built essentially to take care of the poor. In addition note might be made of the existence through the latter part of the nineteenth century of town or city physicians (or in Newark, district physicians) who were paid for their attention to the poor.

Specific enabling legislation for such activities was not enacted until the present century, however.

Medical and hospital care for the indigent thus developed in a rather haphazard way that often reflected the old notion that pauperism was the fault of the pauper. Not until late in the nineteenth century did either humanitarianism or economics effect a change in this attitude. Morever, there had never been either uniformity or agreement among localities. Even after revisions of the New Jersey Poor Law in 1911 and 1924 the basic concept of municipal responsibility, and diversity, was retained, and the laws presented "few barriers to the continuation of nineteenth century municipal poor relief methods." As county, state, and federal agencies came into the picture, the situation became even more confused.

Thus a Commission to Study the Administration of Public Medical Care was created in 1956 and reported in 1959 that a "chaotic mass of law [made it] virtually impossible for anyone to understand or clearly define such matters as medical care responsibility, amounts of payment, payment for service and other technical areas." Indeed anyone who has looked into the situation can readily believe the verdict of the Commission that "the current legislation was of no value in defining the responsibility for providing medical care for the needy and the medically needy."

Involved in this problem was more than administrative overlapping and ineffectiveness. It involved the economic well-being of the hospital as an institution, for if the hospital must find ways to support the medically indigent, then the hospital costs must continue to go up. In turn, as we have noted elsewhere, this must affect Blue Cross rates, which in turn may force fringe groups into the medically indigent brackets and give momentum to a vicious cycle. But even more important, it involved the health, welfare, and rehabilitation of a sizable portion of our society. For 1959 it was estimated that approximately sixty-three thousand hospital admissions a year in New Jersey required or received financial assistance of one kind or another.

The Committee consequently made certain far-reaching recommendations, and apparently went so far as to go directly to the public with its program. Its recommendations for the establishment of a bureau of medical affairs within the Division of Welfare of the Department of Institutions and Agencies was finally incorporated into the 1963 statute by which the State participates in the Kerr-Mills program. Its specific recommendations for changes in the methods of payment for services were not followed, but the "qualified expert" in charge of the bureau under the 1963 statute has the responsibility of negotiating plans, agreements, and fees schedules, and also, as recommended, of carrying on a continuing survey of facilities and of providing professional and technical advice.

MATERNAL AND CHILD HEALTH

New Jersey was one of the earliest states to organize a Division of Child Hygiene in 1915, when one was established within the State Department of Health. Concerned at first with little more than preparing exhibits on child hygiene, the Division was reorganized as a Bureau in 1918 with Dr. Julius Levy, who had been Director of the Division of Child Hygiene of the Newark Department of Health, as "Consultant." In 1918 the Bureau received an appropriation of $125,000 from the legislature, the largest amount ever received by any single bureau in the Department before that time, and, it was believed, the largest appropriation made for the protection of mothers and infants by any state. Clearly there was concern with the great numbers of maternal, neo-natal (under one month), and infant (under one year) deaths.

The Bureau of Child Hygiene began an intensive campaign and, with Dr. Levy as Chief until his retirement in 1951, activity of the same sort has never been discontinued. A nursing service of "child hygiene" nurses was organized, some in State employ, others in local employ, but all co-ordinated at the State level. Their major activity was visiting expectant mothers, infants, and children and offering care, advice, and education. A program of supervision and education of midwives was inaugurated, for although Dr. Levy was aware that the record of infant mortality was better in the practice of midwives than it was in the practice of physicians or in hospital practice, there was obviously much good to be done here. In 1918 it was estimated that over 42 per cent of births were delivered by midwives.

The Bureau also co-ordinated and supervised Baby Keep-Well Stations and soon noted 50 such stations in the State. It created a Division of Education and Extension that worked with schools, school boards, and teachers, and a variety of civic agencies.

The results of this program were salutary, but hardly spectacular. Mothers who received prenatal supervision from the Bureau, and their babies, fared better in the statistics than those who did not receive such supervision. But for the first eight months of 1919, neo-natal deaths were 44.8 per 1000 live births in the State.

Very clearly the physician himself had to be reached, and there is no aspect of public health in which the value of professional self-discipline and self-improvement was more dramatically demonstrated than this. The profession concentrated at first on the maternal death aspect of the problem. The rate of maternal deaths, that is deaths associated with childbirth, in the United States was high, at times the highest in the world. The medical profession was keenly aware of this situation and much concerned with it as the literature of the twenties makes clear.

The leaders of the movement for maternal welfare in New Jersey were Dr. Theodore Teimer of Newark and Dr. Arthur W. Bingham of East Orange. In 1923 the Medical Commission for Maternal Welfare was established by the Essex County Medical Society under the direction of Dr. Bingham. The Commission divided its work into segments. One committee organized prenatal work in various parts of the county using as models a

New York program and the Maternal Center already in existence in the Oranges. Its hospital committee gathered statistics that had a salutary effect in reducing the number of Caesarean sections, a procedure which was being "unwisely overdone," and which "added much to maternal mortality" at the time. An educational committee dealt with the public as well as the profession, and a "followup" committee investigated every maternal death in the county. The effects were worth the effort. In Essex County maternal deaths per thousand live births fell from 6.9 in 1923 to 4.4 in 1934 and in Newark from 7.4 to 4.5.

The success of the Essex County Society induced that group to propose that the State follow suit, and in 1931 the Medical Society of New Jersey created its own Committee on Maternal Welfare. The Committee was to encourage the formation of county commissions, to coordinate the efforts of such committees, and annually report to the Society on its activities.

Under the chairmanship of Dr. Bingham the State Committee mounted a strenuous and continuous campaign. Dr. Bingham himself wrote regularly for the *Journal*. His annual reports, illustrated with maps and graphs, demanded attention; each stark and concise "Lesson from a Death Certificate" that he wrote ended with a direct and pointed question or comment. "Could not an elective cesarean have been done earlier? It would have been safer," was the way he ended lesson "Number Twenty-Two." Altogether 57 such lessons appeared, 52 of them by Dr. Bingham prior to his death in 1943. The Committee also sponsored a series of original articles on obstetrics. Eleven such articles appeared in 1940, for example, and altogether 87 were published before the series ended in 1944.

In 1936 the State Department of Health converted its Bureau of Child Hygiene to one on Maternal and Child Health. With it the State Medical Society cooperated fully. Support came from federal sources and from the State, and 16 "field physicians" were appointed and annual conferences held. The field physicians had both an educational function—to bring instruction and information to fellow physicians, nurses, and the public—and a supervisory one. The latter included checking on hospital practices and, perhaps most significant, investigating each maternal death.

The proof of the effectiveness of these campaigns was to be found in the constantly improving statistics of maternal mortality in the State. In 1931 maternal deaths had stood at 5.9 deaths per 1000 live births, in 1941 they stood at 2.6 and in 1951 at 0.7.

Progress in pediatric care—the mother's milk bank established at Newark about 1928 is worthy of note—and the progress in saving the lives of mothers by proper prenatal and obstetric care were of course reflected in the saving of infant life. Neo-natal deaths in 1961 were 18.5 per 1000 live births; in 1919 they had been 44.8. There was a feeling that victory had been won as early as 1951, not by the "waving of some magic wand, or the use of some wonder drug," but by arduous and intelligent application of sound obstetrical and pediatric practice.

The Problem of the Aging

The improved life expectancy of the modern man has meant of course the aging of our population. The aged citizen presents many problems, not the least of which is the maintenance of his health, and being cared for in case of incapacity. Chronic illness is essentially and particularly the problem of old age.

Except for an abortive attempt at State aid for the indigent chronic sick in 1911, the concern for them was at first a matter for private philanthropy. In 1939, for example, a Committee of the New Jersey Health and Welfare Conference expressed interest in chronic illness, not as a function of aging, but rather as a function of poverty. Organized medicine took an interest in 1948 when the Essex County Medical Society established an

Essex County Service for Chronically Ill that was financed by private individuals.

In 1952 the Medical Society of New Jersey and the Department of Health jointly sponsored the Governor's Conference on Prevention of Chronic Illness. Out of it came legislation that set up a Division of Chronic Illness Control and an Advisory Council on the Chronic Sick as a division of the State Department of Health. This division was authorized to expend funds on the detection and control of disease, the provision of nursing service, housekeeping aid, and rehabilitation. There is also in the State a Division on Aging, established by law in 1957, which is in the Department of State and which is charged with co-ordinating all programs on aging. Its concern is mainly sociological and economic, but it has looked into hospital, nursing, and medical cost problems as well.

The 1961 Report of the Division of Chronic Illness Control speaks of its activities as having "centered in demonstration, case-finding, coordination and consultation service, educational programs, and evaluation studies." Behind this quiet listing there was actually a very great amount of activity, carried out by local agencies with the advice and direction of the Division and with $400,000 in grants-in-aid. Twenty-one hospitals, twelve homemaker agencies, and six other institutions—including Seton Hall College of Medicine—received such grants-in-aid. More specifically studies of alcoholism, arthritis, cancer, glaucoma, leukemia, diabetes, neurological disorders, cardiovascular diseases, mental health, and other medical proglems of the aging have been supported by this Division.

The problem of the aging in obtaining medical and hospital services in an inflationary economy is a serious one. That it should have unleashed a clash between various social forces is hardly surprising. There are those who oppose the State's participation in the Kerr-Mills program which Congress had provided because they contend that it is based on old concepts of pauperization, and who favor a program of health insurance attached to the federal Social Security System. The labor unions are in this group. Their opponents reject such federal health insurance as socialized medicine. The medically indigent are always cared for, they contend, the others in our society can readily prepare for contingency out of their own budgets. The private insurance companies and organized medicine are in this latter group. The Medical-Surgical Plan of New Jersey has made no bones about the fact that its liberalizing of the conditions under which the older citizens could gain protection came in 1962 as a consequence of "pressure for socialized health care of the elderly." Blue Shield, it was stated, "offered the one effective vehicle for preserving the voluntary system."

THE MENTALLY DISTURBED AND DEFICIENT

The advent of tranquilizing drugs has not had the startling effect of suddenly emptying the mental hospitals that has been sensationally reported elsewhere. The number of patients in State and county mental hospitals reached a high of 22,001 in 1957; in 1962 the number was 21,269. There is no doubt that the ratio of patient discharges has improved, from 19 per cent in 1957 to 28 per cent in 1960 and 1961 at the Essex County Overbrook Hospital, for example, but the total number of patients obviously shows no sharp change.

This is because the admission of the aged constitutes a constant, although not a new, problem: 41 per cent of Overbrook's admissions in 1961 were of persons aged over sixty; 30 per cent were of persons aged over seventy. Senile psychiatric patients account for between 30 and 40 per cent of all admissions at Overbrook; in the State hospitals they constitute 20 per cent.

New Jersey still relies heavily on county hospitals for the care of its mental patients. The two nineteenth-century State hospitals, Trenton and Greystone, were independently operated until the Department of Institutions and Agencies was created in 1918. Both hospitals underwent a modernization program in the 1920's. In 1931 a third State mental hospital was opened at Marlboro in Monmouth County, where the cottage group idea was put into practice. In 1955, a fourth hospital, at Ancora in Camden County, accepted its first patient.

In some respects the care of the insane in New Jersey has not kept pace with the needs or with modern psychiatric progress. In 1953, one critic contended that most of the county hospitals were "remnants of almshouses" and provided "no consistent psychiatric equipment." A national summary of Hill-Burton State plan data as of January 1, 1963 indicated that although New Jersey ranked sixth among the states in acceptable beds for mental patients in proportion to population, the State had made provision for only 62.8 per cent of its total needs in this respect. Perhaps the most damaging indictment was the loss of approval for residency training by two of the three State hospitals for a time in the 1950's and the accreditation of the Essex County Overbrook Hospital in 1961 for only two of the three years required in postgraduate psychiatric education.

New Jersey has also been criticized for not having developed a co-ordinated state system for psychiatric service. But the State has nonetheless done a great deal—some of it original and highly significant—in the provision of such services. Each of the State hospitals is the center of psychiatric services for its district. At the Trenton Hospital there is a Diagnostic Center and a Mental Hygiene Bureau. Traveling mental hygiene clinics were established at Trenton and Greystone Park as early as 1921. The Essex County Overbrook Hospital administers the adult mental hygiene clinic in the county.

The major advances were, however, in the field of the psychiatry of the child and youth. In 1920, when child psychiatry was first being developed, the Trenton State Hospital began to provide psychiatric services to State correctional institutions, including the boys' reformatory at Jamesburg. In 1923 the Essex County Juvenile Clinic (now the Essex County Child Guidance Center) had earned a national reputation, and led to the establishment of a Department of Child Guidance in the Newark school system, "a full blown psychiatric clinic." There followed a number of other agencies interested in the child. The children's unit at Marlboro State Hospital was one of the pioneers in the provision of separate hospital facilities for children, and in 1946 New Jersey "led the way in establishing an entirely separate unit," the Arthur Brisbane Child Treatment Center. In 1949 there was established the Diagnostic Center at Menlo Park to deal with the youthful offender. In 1950 an original and distinctive experimental program in group living and therapy for selected youthful male offenders was begun at Highfields near Hopewell. It has become the model for similar experiments, and its success is attested to by the recent establishment of Turrell for girls at Allaire, and of Essexfields in Newark. Essexfields is an urban adaptation of the Highfields approach, using group therapy with youthful offenders who live at home and who may even go to work. Both Turrell and Essexfields are in the main privately operated institutions.

Out of a combination of the interests of Dr. S. Olin Garrison of the Training School at Vineland, and of Dr. John Ward at the Trenton State Hospital, New Jersey has given special attention to epileptics since 1898. In that year the New Jersey State Village of Epileptics, inspired by the famous "Epileptic Colony" at Bielefeld, Germany, was founded. New Jersey was thus one of a few states that recognized that epileptics required a different kind of care from that provided by either the mental hospital or the training school. The State Village, sometimes known by the name of its location, Skillman, became the New Jersey Neuro-Psychiatric Institute in 1953.

New Jersey's early fame in the treatment of children came not from the efforts of psychiatric institutions but from the training schools for mental defectives. Men like Edward R. Johnstone and H. H. Goddard earned acclaim for themselves and the Vineland Training School with which they were associated early in this century. Their work was experimental, custodial, and educative, rather than medical, and the State has continued this kind of attention to the mental defective.

In 1956 a State Commission on Mental Health was established which thoroughly surveyed all ramifications of the problems of the mentally ill and retarded. Its report in 1961 showed a deep concern for these unfortunates. It recommended a consolidation of existing statutes and a reform of administrative procedures not only to facilitate the care of the patients but also to protect their civil liberties. Specifically, the Commission recommended that facilities for diagnosis, care, and treatment of the mentally ill be readily available to all who needed it, and that primary emphasis be placed on rehabilitation. The simplification of procedure for voluntary entrance and withdrawal from mental hospitals was also recommended, and more attention to the provision of pre- and post-hospitalization services to outpatients was requested.

In 1963, a "Mental Health Act" proposing a general revision of the laws governing mental health in the light of these recommendations was approved by the Assembly, but after a full year's grinding in the legislative mill, it died in the Senate. The bill has been reintroduced in the current legislature (1964).

XIV

MICROCOSM

T HERE IS SOMETHING OF A TEMPTATION to conclude this account with a statistical analysis of the health facilities and accomplishments of New Jersey as it enters its fourth century. But such statistics may or may not be meaningful. Does the number of physicians, or the number of hospital beds have any significance in a state still hemmed in by Philadelphia and New York? Does the greater portion of New Jerseymen who are covered by Blue Cross-Blue Shield necessarily prove they are getting better service for the price they pay? Does the fact that the death rate is now at its lowest point in history, or does the drop in the incidence of poliomyelitis, or does the improvement in the rate of natal deaths, or does the increase in life expectancy reflect any condition or activity peculiar to New Jersey? Is there any way of determining that any of these rates would be better (from the social point of view) had some State or professional activity been different?

Clearly unequivocal answers are not possible. Suffice it here to point out again, however, that complacency is not warranted, and that much remains to be accomplished.

It is beyond the scope of this historical study to point out what needs to be done. The temptation is great to suggest that the State has not entirely gone beyond its nineteenth-century reliance on its neighbors. New Jersey finally overcame its dependence on others in the care of the blind and the feeble-minded. She finally built her own hospitals, and she has even reached the point of educating her own physicians. But if she really wishes to do the last it will have to mean a loosening of the governmental purse strings. The temptation is great also to point out that there are only five local boards of health in the State whose full-time chiefs are medical doctors, and that no substantial progress seems to be made by any other agency, public or private, toward the spread of such multiple-screening programs as that at the Hunterdon Medical Center.

It would perhaps be more appropriate for this study to end with a discussion of New Jersey as the microcosm, not simply of medical history, but of the whole of American civilization.

Perhaps the most discernible facet of American life disclosed by this study has been the slow but certain tendency toward the increasing reliance upon organization and authority to meet the problems of the times. Wherever we were to glance back in this account we would find that this had happened. It happened as early as 1772 when the licensing of physicians was first promulgated. It happened with insane asylums, with hospitals, with boards of health.

We find too that this tendency has regularly met with resistance, a resistance not the result only of inertia or self-interest, though these were often present, but a resistance stemming from the belief that something was being lost. Individuality, freedom, personal integrity seemed to be at stake, and perhaps there is no better example of this than the attitude of organized medicine in the State to any further extension of government into medical care, or in organized medicine's resort to prepaid insurance plans to head off such governmental expansion. Critics might contend that individuality and freedom have really nothing to do with this process, that organized medicine is merely seeking to protect its own selfish economic interests. This may be exactly the individuality the physician seeks to maintain, particularly if he feels that better medical attention can be obtained in this way. But the physician seems to be rebelling, too, against what he believes will make him less and less a free agent and more and more a bureaucrat.

Well exemplified in New Jersey, too, was the resort to voluntary organizations to gain one's ends. Medical Society, Sanitarian Association, Tuberculosis Society, Pharmaceutical Association, Osteopathic League, charitable societies in great number, each group found need to organize. But each such organization sooner or later resorted to authority, to the legislature, for protection and support. Each turned into a pressure group, and in seeking its ends each insisted it was acting *pro bono publico*. The interesting thing is that perhaps it was. The lobby may sometimes be a very effective means of protecting the general weal.

The history of medicine and health, moreover, helps explain the reason for this tendency toward organization and authority. Hospitals, the need for sanitation, the care of the sick-poor were all medical and health problems that were a direct consequence of industrialization and urbanization. Examples of such relationships can be multiplied indefinitely, but perhaps more significant was the fact that these were problems arising out of the complexity of our society. They could be solved by no other means than general authority. Mosquito extermination is a case in point, so is water and air pollution, so is the inspection of dairies, so will be problems pertaining to artificial irradiation of the atmosphere. Diseases, smallpox, diphtheria, malaria, poliomyelitis, all defied the knowledge and the skill of the individual doctor. To wipe them out social action was necessary.

Moreover, as we get to learn more, as science and technology advance, the individual is less capable of doing things by himself. The equipment of the large modern hospital, for example, is beyond the capacities of many hospitals, so they must either amalgamate, or seek governmental assistance, or both.

One other element in this history that is a microcosm

of American life can be observed—the slowness of change. The conservative forces in American life can be the same groups who came into existence originally to seek protection for themselves—the Societies and Associations. But as they struggled against change—as the physicians combated the osteopaths in the legislative lobbies, or as organized medicine fought "Contract Plans" in one generation and accepted medical-surgical plans in the next—we achieved a social stability that may make worthwhile the imperfections we must countenance.

One other, and final, consideration. Change does occur; there are always new groups arising that reject the idea of a natural law of progress. Refusing to sit back to wait for progress to happen, they insist upon playing a creative role in its attainment.

SOURCES *

Chapter I

The seventeenth-century letters that are cited are found in *The Model of Government of the Province of East-New-Jersey in America* (Edinburgh, 1685) and *An Abstract, or Abbreviation of some Few of the Many (Later and Former) Testimonys from the Inhabitants of New-Jersey* . . . (London, 1681).

The account of Salem Creek is from James K. Hosmer (ed.), *Winthrop's Journal* (New York, 1908), II, and John E. Pomfret, *The Province of West New Jersey* (Princeton, 1956). The summary of diseases is based on John Duffy, *Epidemics in Colonial America* (Baton Rouge, 1953), and Francis R. Packard, *The History of Medicine in the United States* (Philadelphia, 1901). Other information is from contemporary newspaper accounts.

The Hankinson family commonplace book is in the Rutgers University Library. George B. Griffenhagen and James H. Young have written on "Old English Patent Medicines in America" in the *United States National Museum Bulletin,* No. 218 (1959).

The summaries and tabulations pertaining to the practitioner and his training were developed mainly from the biographic materials in Stephen Wickes, *History of Medicine in New Jersey* (Newark, 1879); John R. Stevenson, "Physicians in the Colonization of New Jersey," *The*

* A typescript of this book containing detailed documentation is on deposit at the Rutgers University Library.

Jerseyman, XI (1905); and William L. Vroom, "Some Early Physicians of Bergen County," *Proceedings of The New Jersey Historical Society,* L (1932). The situation in Great Britain is described by R. S. Roberts, "The Personnel and Practice of Medicine in Tudor and Stuart England," *Medical History,* VI (1962). The incident involving the Anglican Church at Perth Amboy is from a letter of the Church Wardens dated June 16, 1769 in the Society for the Propagation of the Gospel in Foreign Parts Mss., Letters Received, Series B, XXIV, London, of which there are copies in the Rutgers Library. Other details are from Fred B. Rogers, "The Medical Society of New Jersey—Its First Quarter Century," *Journal of the Medical Society of New Jersey,* L (1953), and from *The Rise, Minutes, and Proceedings, of the New Jersey Medical Society* (Newark, 1875). The last will hereafter be referred to as *Transactions 1766-1858.*

Information on Cadwalader is from the *Dictionary of American Biography;* Packard; and E. M. Woodward and J. F. Hageman, *History of Burlington and Mercer Counties* (Philadelphia, 1883).

The section on early education is derived from Wickes; Anon., "The Medical Society of New Jersey," *Journal of the Medical Society of New Jersey,* XXXVIII (1941); and David D. Demarest, *Rutgers (Queen's) College and Medical Degrees* (Trenton, 1894). The discussion of dissection is based on material in Stevenson; Packard; Frederick C. Waite, "The Development of Anatomical Laws in the States of New England," *New England Journal of Medicine,* CCXXXIII (1945); and Henry B. Shafer, *The American Medical Profession 1783 to 1850* (New York, 1936).

The New Jersey Historical Society has a manuscript book of minutes of the New Jersey Medical Society. The details of the medical organization are almost entirely from the printed Medical Society *Transactions 1766-1858.*

The account of early licensure uses Packard; Richard H. Shryock, *Medicine and Society in America 1660-1860* (New York, 1960); James T. Adams, *Provincial Society*

(New York, 1927); and Gurdon W. Russell, *Early Medicine, and Early Medical Men in Connecticut* (n.p., 1892). The Smith and Wade licenses are in Volume AAA of Commissions, Secretary of State Office, Trenton. The petitions are described by Mildred V. Naylor, "A New Jersey Petition," *Bulletin of the History of Medicine,* XVII (1945), and Fred B. Rogers, "A Colonial Petition to Improve Medical Practice in New Jersey," *Academy of Medicine of New Jersey Bulletin,* V, no. 2 (1959).

The sections on science and the theory and practice of medicine represent mainly a synthesis of materials from the *Transactions* of the Medical Society. Such items are usually dated. Other sources of information were William Pierson, "Historical Narrative," *Transactions of the Medical Society of New Jersey, 1866;* the inventory of the estate of Dr. John Roberts of Burlington, January 16, 17, 1723 (in the Office of the N. J. Clerk of the Superior Court); Dr. Jonathan Smith's contributions, listed in the *Charter, Laws, and Catalogue of the Books of the Library Company of Burlington* (Philadelphia, 1758); the broadside "A Catalogue of Medicines Sold by Mr. Robert Talbot at Burlington," in The New Jersey Historical Society; Stevenson; and David L. Cowen, *America's Pre-Pharmacopoeial Literature* (Madison, 1961). The description of Dr. Elmer's therapeutics is based on Wickes. The dictum of contempt for the eighteenth-century practitioner is quoted by Shryock.

The references to the development of medical theory in general are from either Richard H. Shryock *The Development of Modern Medicine* (New York, 1947) or Lester S. King, *The Medical World of the Eighteenth Century* (Chicago, 1958).

CHAPTER II

This chapter is almost wholly a synthesis of materials found in the *Transactions* of the Medical Society for the years cited. The *Country Practitioner* is another source used, and, except for certain references to Dr. Page and Dr. Michener, is specifically mentioned in the text. Dr. Page's paper appeared in Volume I (1879); Dr. Michener's in Volume II (1881).

In addition, Dr. Alex Berman, "The Thompsonian Movement and Its Relation to American Pharmacy and Medicine," *Bulletin of the History of Medicine*, XXV (1951) is used. John R. Stevenson, *The History of Medicine and Medical Men of Camden County, New Jersey* (Philadelphia, 1886) is the source of the statement on the decline of the practice of bleeding in that county. Oliver W. Holmes' attitude toward the materia medica can be found in his "Border Lines in Medical Science," *Medical Essays 1842-1882* (Boston, 1883). The early interest in the germ theory of disease follows Shryock, *The Development of Modern Medicine*.

CHAPTER III

This chapter is also largely a synthesis of materials in the *Transactions* for the years cited. Some use has again been made of the *Country Practitioner*. The references to Newark come mainly from Edgar Holden *Mortality and Sanitary Record of Newark, New Jersey* (n.p., n.d., [1880]) and Anon., "The Climatology and Diseases of Essex County," *Transactions of the Medical Society of New Jersey, 1887*. The references to Camden are mainly from Stevenson's history of medicine in that county. Of considerable help was Joseph A. Vasselli, "A Pestilence Census-Taker in New Jersey," *Bulletin of the History of Medicine*, XXV (1951). The tuberculosis figures from 1879 to 1898 are from the annual report of the State Board of Health for the latter year. The historical details of diphtheria generally are from C. Singer and E. A. Underwood, *A Short History of Medicine* (New York, 1962).

Regarding Vandeveer, see Wickes and also James Thacher, *The American New Dispensatory* (4th ed.;

Boston, 1821). Regarding veratrum viride, Thacher; William Cullen, *A Treatise of the Materia Medica* (Dublin, 1789), II; and H. C. Wood, *et al., Dispensatory of the United States* (15th ed.; Philadelphia, 1883) are used.

The introduction of the hypodermic needle in 1844 is discussed by Shryock, *The Development of Modern Medicine.*

CHAPTER IV

The *Transactions* are again the chief source for this chapter. There are a few references from the *Country Practitioner*. The source of those items derived from the statutes is self-evident.

Richard H. Shryock, *American Medical Research* (New York, 1947) is the source of the statement regarding the lack of originality in medical research, and for the quotation from Comte. The references to Auenbrugger and Laennec are derived from Bernhard J. Stern, *Society and Medical Progress* (Princeton, 1941) and from Singer and Underwood. The introduction of the thermometer follows Shryock, *The Development of Modern Medicine,* and Stern. The reference to Dr. Larison is from Harry B. Weiss, *Country Dr. Cornelius Wilson Larison* (Trenton, 1953). The reference to Vierordt and the sphygmograph is from Singer and Underwood. The late use of microscopes in medical schools follows Stern. The information on the New Brunswick Society is from the *New Jersey State Microscopical Society, The Forty-Fifth Anniversary Meeting* (n. p., c. 1914); the information on the Camden Society is from the *Country Practitioner,* I (1879). Dr. Joseph Parrish's view on alcoholism is from his *Alcoholic Inebriety from a Medical Standpoint* (Philadelphia, 1883).

The information on the New Jersey Academy of Medicine is from the *Constitution and By-Laws with the Act of Incorporation and List of Fellows of the New Jersey Academy of Medicine* (Jersey City, 1875); from various issues of the *Medical Directory of New York, New Jersey, and Connecticut* and of the *Medical Register of New York, New Jersey, and Connecticut;* and from contemporary newspaper notices.

The delay in the spread of Lister's teaching is mentioned by Shryock, *Development of Modern Medicine.* The discussion of the use of bromide of ethyl is found in the *Country Practitioner,* I (1880).

The operations by Drs. Cutter and Brumley were reported by the *Newark Daily Advertiser* on November 14, 1865 and January 3, 1862 respectively, and the use of the laryngoscope in a throat operation was reported by the same paper on March 12, 1885.

In the section on "Specialization in Medicine" a good deal of the information comes from contemporary issues of the *Newark Daily Advertiser.* Most helpful in this regard was the compilation under the supervision of Samuel Berg of the accounts of *Medical Practice and Hospital Development in Newark, New Jersey 1850-1887 as Reported in the Newark Daily Advertiser.* A typescript of this compilation is in the Newark Public Library. For a general consideration of the topic, see George Rosen, *The Specialization of Medicine* (New York, 1944). The quotation on the merging of medicine and surgery in America , is from William Meade's introduction to his edition of James Wilson, *Pharmacopoeia Chirurgica* (Philadelphia, 1818). For Dr. Coit's biography see the *Journal of the Medical Society of New Jersey,* XIV (1917). For the antagonism between the general practitioner and the specialist, see Shryock, *The Development of Modern Medicine.*

CHAPTER V

The information on medical economics is derived from the *Transactions;* the *Country Practitioner;* J. Henry Clark, *The First Fifty Years of the District Society of Essex County* (Newark, 1867); and Weiss.

The history of the licensing laws is derived from the *Transactions;* Elias J. Marsh, "An Outline History of the Medical Society of New Jersey to 1903," *Proceedings of The New Jersey Historical Society,* LX (1942); Pierson; and Fred B. Rogers, "To Repeal All Medical Laws," *Journal of the Medical Society of New Jersey,* LVI (1959).

For the story of "Neo-Thompsonianism in the United States" see an article by that title by Alex Berman, *Journal of the History of Medicine and Allied Sciences,* XI (1956). Besides the Newark Directories, the material on Dr. Robinson is from William H. Shaw, *History of Essex and Union Counties* (Philadelphia, 1884) and the *Transactions of the Eclectic Medical Society of New Jersey for . . . 1876 and 1877.*

On the general *rapprochement* between allopaths, homeopaths, and eclectics, see Shryock, *Development of Modern Medicine.* The election of a homeopath to the Camden Medical Society in 1908 is taken from Anon., *Camden County Medical Society 1846-1956* (Camden, 1957).

The statutory references are derived from the statute books for the years cited, not from the *Transactions.*

The statistics of the education of practitioners are from the *Transactions;* the *Country Practitioner;* and Stevenson, *History of Medicine . . . of Camden County.* The general educational developments in the country are taken from Shafer, and Stern.

The account of New Jersey educational efforts is from John Maclean, *History of the College of New Jersey* (Philadelphia, 1877), II; and Demarest. The early suggestion of a college of medicine in Newark is from the *Newark Daily Advertiser* of December 2, 1872. All other details are from the *Transactions.*

The material on the mushrooming of medical schools comes from Stevenson, *History of Medicine . . . of Camden County;* unpublished material supplied by Harold J. Abrahams; *Corporations of New Jersey List of Certificates to Dec. 31, 1911* (Trenton, 1914); New Jersey statutes; and the *First Annual Report* (1891) of the State

Board of Medical Examiners. The Eliot quotation is from Stern. The Sweet and Robinson misspellings are from their manuscript Record Book, 1856-1866, at The New Jersey Historical Society.

CHAPTER VI

The general philosophy of the Sanitary Movement is derived from Rene Dubos, *Mirage of Health* (New York, 1939) and George Rosen, *A History of Public Health* (New York, 1958).

The *Transactions* again form the basic source of the material presented, but conditions in the municipalities are derived from Holden; Vaselli; the *Country Practitioner;* newspaper accounts; and Lott Southard, "Essex Water Supply," *Transactions of the Medical Society of New Jersey, 1877*.

The basic substance of the discussion of water and sewerage is also from the *Transactions. Shall We Continue to Use the Sewage Polluted Passaic; or Shall We Get Pure Water?* (Jersey City, 1887) and William S. Disbrow, "A Municipal Moloch," *Transactions of the Medical Society of New Jersey, 1899,* are also used. The sources for the discussion of water purification are Nelson M. Blake, *Water for the Cities* (Syracuse, 1956) and M. N. Baker, *The Quest for Pure Water* (New York, 1948).

The discussion of boards of health is derived from the *Transactions* and New Jersey statutes. Official reports like that of the Health Commission for 1874 and the *Twentieth Annual Report of the Board of Health* (1896) are also used. *The New Jersey Health and Sanitary Association 1875-1949* (Newark, 1949) is the basic reference to that association. The account of the State Board of Health relies on Anon., "Development of State Health Administration," *Public Health News*, XXVIII (1947).

The biographical material on Ezra Hunt is based on Wilson G. Smillie, "The Great Pioneers of Public Health in America," *American Journal of Public Health* XLIII

(1953), and especially, Fred B. Rogers, *Help-Bringers* (New York, 1960).

The Vaccine Institute at Paterson is mentioned by Shafer and the one at Newark in the *Newark Daily Advertiser* of March 26, 1858. The Hudson County Sanitary Code is to be found in *The Medical Register of New York, New Jersey, and Connecticut,* XIII (1875). Other material is from the *Transactions,* the *Country Practitioner,* and the State statutes.

The Sandy Hook quarantine problem was publicized in: *Correspondence Relating to the Quarantine Subject, between . . . Marcus L. Ward Gov. of New Jersey, Hon. W. A. Newell, and Gen. J. H. Martindale* (Trenton, 1867), and *Communication from the Governor of New York, Transmitting a Communication from the Governor of New Jersey . . . relative to Quarantine Jurisdiction* (Albany, 1875).

Quarantine measures are mentioned by Vaselli. Anon., *Some Account of the Orange Training School for Nurses* (Orange, 1899) tells of the isolation ward of the Orange Memorial Hospital. The Morristown broadside, which is at the Rutgers Library, is undated, and begins "Notice The following regulations have been adopted by the Board of Health."

CHAPTER VII

The basic sources for the section on hospitals and nursing are the statutes of the State, the *Newark Daily Advertiser,* and to a lesser extent, the *Transactions.*

The 30 hospitals in Paris are mentioned by Shryock, *Development of Modern Medicine.* The revolutionary hospitals are mentioned by Wickes; Clark; Frank J. Urquhart, *A History of the City of Newark* (New York, 1913), I; Fred B. Rogers, "The Old Barracks at Trenton," *Journal of the Medical Society of New Jersey,* LV (1958); and W. Woodford Clayton, *History of Union and Middlesex Counties* (Philadelphia, 1882).

As indicated by the titles of the following, a great deal of the history of hospitals named came from other sources than the statutes and newspapers: Catalogue of the School of Nursing of the Jersey City Hospital, 1963-1964; *Some Account of the Orange Training School for Nurses; Camden County Medical Society* (for Cooper Hospital); *History of the Clara Maass Memorial Hospital* (Mimeo.); the *Ninety-Second Annual Report of the Paterson General Hospital* (Paterson, 1962); Public Relations Department of St. Michael Hospital Memorandum, March 5, 1963; Public Relations Department of St. Joseph's Hospital Memorandum April, 1963; Memorandum from A. O. Davidson of Christ Hospital, April 5, 1963; *The Monitor*, October 26, 1962 (for St. Francis of Trenton). Useful also were J. Harold Johnston, "Down the Past," *Fast Facts*, II (May, 1961), and Rosary S. Gilheany, "The Hospitals in Newark," a typescript at the New Jersey Academy of Medicine.

The 1904 hospital statistics are from the U. S. Census Special Report on Benevolent Institutions of that year.

For the motivations behind the establishment of nursing schools, see Richard H. Shryock, *The History of Nursing* (Philadelphia, 1959). Specific details of the schools involved are from the following: Gilheany (German Hospital); *Some Account of the Orange Training School for Nurses; Fifty Years of Service to Mankind, 1882-1932* (Paterson General); *Second Annual Announcement of the Training School for Nurses . . . Cooper Hospital* (1890-1891); Christ Hospital School of Nursing Catalogue, 1962; and Public Relations Department of St. Joseph's Hospital Memorandum, April 1963.

Dorothea Dix's actions and statements are from Helen E. Marshall, *Dorothea Dix* (Chapel Hill, 1937). For New Jersey's earlier attention to the blind and deaf see Adelaide R. Haase, *Index of . . . Documents . . . of . . . New Jersey* (Washington, 1914).

The activity in the State before the arrival of Miss Dix is taken from the *Transactions; Report of a Select Committee of the Legislative Council . . . on . . . a State Luna-*

tic Asylum (Trenton, 1839); *Report of the Commissioners Appointed by the Governor . . . to Ascertain the Number of Lunatics and Idiots in the State* (Newark, 1840; reprinted, Trenton, 1841); *Report Relative to an Asylum for Lunatics by the Joint Committee of Council and Assembly* (Trenton, 1841); Journal of the Legislative Council, 65th Session, 1st Sitting, 1840; and Votes and Proceedings of the Assembly, 65th Session, 1st Sitting, 1840.

Miss Dix's main effort was the *Memorial Soliciting a State Hospital for the Insane, Submitted to the Legislature of New Jersey, January 23, 1845* (Trenton, 1845). The fame of the building is derived from Shafer. The "moral treatment" can be found spelled out in *By-Laws Adopted by the Managers of the New Jersey State Lunatic Asylum . . . 1847* (Trenton, 1848).

The description of the inability of the Trenton hospital to cope with the demands is derived from the *Transactions* and the *Country Practitioner*. The claim of the Essex County hospital to being the largest in the country was made in a letter to the author from Dr. Henry A. Davidson of that hospital, dated April 1, 1963. The dates of the development of county hospitals are taken from the *Journal of the American Hospital Association*, XXVI, No. 15, Pt. 2 (1962). The "Trenton Observer" mentioned was Dr. Horace G. Wetherill who published *The Insane and the Asylums* (Trenton, 1892).

The county hospital situation and the 1900 statistics are taken from the *Fifty-Third Annual Report* of the Trenton Hospital (1900) and the *Twenty-Fifth Annual Report* of the Morris Plains Hospital (1900). The critics of the hospitals were Wetherill and J. L. Bodine, *The Management of the Insane* (n.p., 1876).

CHAPTER VIII

In "Measuring the Advance" almost all of the statistics are derived from the *Twenty-Fourth Annual Report of the Board of Health of . . . New Jersey 1900* (Trenton, 1901). *The Historical Statistics of the United States 1789-*

1945 (Washington, 1949) is also cited. The use of diphtheria antitoxin is recounted in the *Transactions* for 1896. The Camden experience with typhoid fever is from the *Transactions* for 1900.

CHAPTER IX

The sources of this chapter are very largely based on materials in the *Transactions* and the *Journal of the Medical Society of New Jersey*. The references to blood transfusions are derived from William G. Bernhard, "Fifty Years of Pathology and Clinical Pathology in New Jersey," and Christopher A. Beling, "Fifty Years of Surgery in New Jersey," both in the *Academy of Medicine of New Jersey Bulletin,* VII (1961).

The mortality statistics are from the *Fifty-Ninth Annual Report of the Department of Health* (Trenton, 1936). The tuberculosis story is based on William J. Ellis, "Public Welfare in New Jersey, 1630-1944," in William S. Myers, *The Story of New Jersey* (New York, 1945), II. The statement with regard to national experience with tuberculosis is based on figures in the *Historical Statistics of the United States* (Washington, 1960). The influenza story is told in Henry A. Davidson, "New Jersey and the Great Pandemic," *Journal of the Medical Society of New Jersey,* LIV (1957).

On the advent of the new chemotherapeutic agents and antibiotics see Rowland D. Goodman, II, "Fifty Years of Pharmacology," *Journal of the Medical Society of New Jersey,* L (1953). The statistics on the contemporary scene are adapted from the 84th (1961), 39th (1915) and 59th (1936) *Annual Report* of the Department of Health.

CHAPTER X

The *Journal* of the State Medical Society is only occasionally the source of details in this chapter. Samuel Berg has told the story of "The Essex County Pathologic and

Anatomic Society" in the *Journal*, LVI (1959); Julius Gerendasy has written "The History of the New Jersey Gastroenterological Society" also in the *Journal*, L (1953); The Academy of Medicine of New Jersey has been treated by Arthur J. D'Alessandro, "The First Fifty Years," and by Morris H. Saffron, "The Academy as a Cultural Force in New Jersey," both in the *Academy of Medicine of New Jersey Bulletin*, VII, No. 2 (1961). The early libraries are listed in the *Medical Directory of New York, New Jersey, and Connecticut*, X (1908).

The section on surgery is derived largely from Beling. The surgery performed at St. Peter's in 1910 is recounted in the *Journal*, VII (1911). "Eagleton's technic" is described in Frederick Christopher, *A Textbook of Surgery* (4th ed.; Philadelphia, 1945). Eagleton's "An Original Device for the Control of Hemorrhage from the Large Sinuses of the Brain . . ." appeared in the *Journal*, XVI (1919). The story of "Cardiovascular Surgery at St. Michael's Hospital" was told by Anthony D. Crecca in the *Journal*, L (1953).

The account of the changes in legal requirements was developed from the *Transactions*, the *Journal*, and, especially, the New Jersey statutes. The 1903 situation is taken from E. L. B. Godfrey, "The Educational Standards of the Medical Profession of New Jersey," *Transactions, 1903;* the pharmaceutical legislation from David L. Cowen, "The New Jersey Pharmaceutical Association, 1870-1945," *New Jersey Journal of Pharmacy*, XVIII (1945).

The sources of the discussion of medical sectarianism are also the *Journal* and statutes of New Jersey. The early struggles between the osteopaths and the "regular" profession are described by William C. Bugbee, "Observations in Retrospect," and Thomas L. Northrup, "Gone Are the Days," both in the *New Jersey Association of Osteopathic Physicians and Surgeons Journal*, LXII, No. 3 (1963). The information on osteopathic hospitals is from the *American Osteopathic Association Registry of Hospitals*, July, 1962. Recent court decisions were reported in the *Newark Evening News*, July 2, 1963.

The 1953 statistics relating to chiropractors are from the 63rd (1953) and 64th (1954) *Annual Report* of the State Board of Medical Examiners. I. M. Stewart and A. L. Austen *A History of Nursing* (New York, 1962) places New Jersey among the first four states to require registration of nurses.

Chapter XI

The data on nursing schools are adapted from *Journal American Hospital Association,* XXXVI, Pt. 2 (1962) and the *New Jersey Nurse* 60th Anniversary Special Issue (1962). The information on the college-affiliated schools is from the Seton Hall University General Bulletin, 1961-1962; the Undergraduate Catalog of Fairleigh Dickinson University, 1963-1964; and the Faculty Handbook of the Rutgers College of Nursing.

The history of the Rutgers College of Pharmacy is from the *Rutgers University New Jersey College of Pharmacy Fiftieth Anniversary Commencement 1892-1942* (1943).

Information on the University of New Jersey is mainly from a letter to the author from C. J. Schweikhardt, Secretary of the State Board of Dentistry, August 16, 1963.

The Essex Medical College account is based on contemporary newspaper stories. The history of the movement for a medical school is pieced together from information in the *Journal* of the Medical Society for 1947 and 1948; Stuart Z. Hawkes, *Views on the Establishment of a Medical College in New Jersey* (Mimeo., 1947); various letters in the Rutgers Archives; the *Report of the New Jersey Medical College Commission Appointed Pursuant to Laws of 1950 Joint Resolution No. 4 March 5, 1951;* and Minutes of the Rutgers Board of Trustees for January 25, 1952.

The account of the Referendum of 1954 is based on contemporary newspaper stories.

The Seton Hall College of Medicine and Dentistry data are from a letter to the author from the public relations department of the College and from the College Catalog for 1963-1964. The Fairleigh Dickinson data are from Walter A. Wilson, "A School of Dentistry is Born," *Annals of Dentistry*, XV (1956) and information supplied by the public relations department of Fairleigh Dickinson. The Rutgers School of Medicine data are from a *Proposed Program in Human Biology and Medicine at Rutgers—The State University of New Jersey* (Mimeo., April 28, 1961); Minutes of the Meeting of Committee on a Medical School, Morven, May 16, 1961; and various issues of the *Rutgers Newsletter*.

The account of the research activities of John B. Smith is based on his *Report of the New Jersey State Agricultural Experiment Station upon the Mosquitoes . . .* (Trenton, 1904). That of Waksman is based on a biographical sketch of him issued by the Institute of Microbiology Public Relations Department, January, 1963 (Mimeo.). Other research at Rutgers is based on a memorandum by Willam H. Cole on a "Topical Outline of a Few Research Contributions by Rutgers" (1954), and *The Bureau of Biological Research 1936-56, Rutgers University* (n.p., n.d.).

The Princeton account is from various Princeton Department of Information news releases (1961-1963) and from Jay K. Lucker (ed.), *A Bibliography of Princeton Faculty Publications 1961-62* (Princeton, 1963).

The account of the Rockefeller Institute is based on information from Dr. George W. Corner, author of a history of the Institute to be published by the Rockefeller Institute Press, New York.

The references to research at Fairleigh Dickinson and Seton Hall are from the Catalog of the Fairleigh Dickinson School of Dentistry, 1963-1964-1965; information from the public relations department of Seton Hall; and the 84th *Annual Report* of the Department of Health (1961).

The sources for the account of industrial research are Selman A. Waksman, "A Most Fruitful Connection," *By Their Fruits* (Merck Sharp & Dohme, 1962); Tom Mahoney, *The Merchants of Life* (New York, 1959); *The Serpasil Story* (Mimeo., 1955); news releases of the Squibb Division of Olin Mathieson Chemical Corporation; and Leonard A. Scheele, "The Relentless Search for New Drugs," *New Jersey Business,* VIII, No. 2 (1961).

CHAPTER XII

Hospital figures are derived mainly from the *Journal of the American Hospital Association,* XXXVI, Pt. 2 (1962). References to the federal assistance program are from the *Hill-Burton Program Progress Report July 1, 1947-June 30, 1963,* U. S. Department of Health, Education and Welfare (Washington, 1963). Other information comes from the *Journal* of the Medical Society, but most of it is from a host of ephemeral leaflet and special-release material issued by the hospitals named.

Martland's work is based on George H. Lathrope, "A Half Century of Medicine," *Journal of the Medical Society of New Jersey,* L (1953). Kessler's work is derived from Henry A. Brodkin, "New Jersey Service to the Physically Handicapped," in the same issue of the *Journal;* Beling; and *Who's Who in America.* Levine's work is derived from Bernhard, and *Triangle,* V (1961).

The Hunterdon story is based on Ray E. Trussell, *Hunterdon Medical Center* (Cambridge, 1956), and E. D. Pellegrino "The Role of the Local Community in the Development of Health Services—The Hunterdon Experiment," *Industry and Tropical Health,* IV (1961).

The origins of the Blue Cross plan are described in Louis H. Pink, *The Story of Blue Cross,* Public Affairs Pamphlet No. 101 (1945). The details of the development of the New Jersey Plan are derived from two releases of the Plan: *The Story of Hospital Service Plan of New Jersey* (1962) and *New Jersey Blue Cross Milestones of Progress* (1962). The backgrounds of Blue Shield are based on Edward W. Sprague, "Trends in Medical Care," *Journal of the Medical Society of New Jersey,* L (1953).

Later details are from the Blue Shield Manual for Participating Physicians (1961); the *Medical-Surgical Plan of New Jersey 1962 Annual Statement and Report to the Medical Society of New Jersey* (n.p., n.d.); and stories in the *Newark Evening News* of June 24, 1962 and October 20, 1963.

The more recent problems of Blue Cross–Blue Shield are derived from the Preliminary Report of the New Jersey Blue Cross Study to Commissioner C. R. Howell, March 15, 1959 (Mimeo.); Testimony Presented before C. R. Howell at a Public Hearing on Proposed Blue Cross Rate Increase, by Joel R. Jacobsen, April 12, 1962 (Mimeo.); the *New York Times,* July 2, 1963; and Brief for Appellant, Superior Court of New Jersey, *GHI* vs. *C. R. Howell and Medical-Surgical Plan of New Jersey.*

Chapter XIII

Information on the boards of health derives from the statutes of New Jersey; from the *Thirty-Second Annual Report of the Board of Health* (1908), and the *Journal* of the Medical Society. The recent study referred to is Robert M. Northrop, *Organizing for Public Health* (New Brunswick, 1962). The 1948-1949 reorganization of the Department is from Bennett M. Rich, *The Government of New Jersey* (New York, 1957).

The section on "Sewage and Water Supply" is based mainly on the statutes, but details are used from *Passaic Valley Sewerage Commissioners 1924-1949* (n.p., n.d.); the *Manual of the Legislature of New Jersey 1963* (Trenton, 1963); the Report of the Division of Sewerage and Water Supplies in the *Thirty Second Annual Report of the Board of Health* (1908); and Rich.

The first work on mosquito extermination was John B. Smith, "The Progress of Mosquito Extermination Work in New Jersey," *Proceedings . . . of the New Jersey Sanitary Association . . . 1908* (Trenton, 1909). The role of insects in disease is discussed by Shryock, *Development of Modern Medicine*. The Maass story is told by John

T. Cunningham, "Tercentenary Tales," *The Democrat,* March 28, 1963.

A good deal of information comes from Thomas J. Headlee, *The Mosquitoes of New Jersey and Their Control,* N. J. Agricultural Experiment Station Bulletin 348 (New Brunswick, 1921). The laws of 1902, 1905, 1906, 1912, and 1919 can all be found in Headlee. A revision of Headlee appeared in 1945. The *Journal* of the Medical Society is also quoted. The South Orange story comes from *The Village Improvement Society of South Orange, N. J. Report of Committee on Mosquito Extermination Season of 1902* (n.p., n.d.). More recent details are from the 1st (1956), 4th (1959-60), and 5th (1960-61) *Annual Report* of the State Mosquito Control Commission.

The section on the sick-poor is derived from Ellis; from the statutes; from the leaflet *10 Steps Forward,* Digest of Report to the N. J. Commission to Study . . . Public Medical Care (1959); and the *Report and Recommendation of the New Jersey Commission to Study the Administration of Public Medical Care* (Trenton, 1959).

The early history of the Division of Child Hygiene is from Emily S. Hamblen, "Public Health and Child Hygiene," *Journal of the Medical Society of New Jersey,* XVI (1919). The 41st (1917), 42nd (1919), 59th (1936), 60th (1937), and 84th (1961) *Annual Report of the Department of Health* are also used. The *Public Health News,* IV (1918-1919) is the source of the information concerning infant deaths in 1919. For the awareness of the medical profession of the high incidence of maternal deaths see, for example, the *American Journal of Obstetrics and Gynecology,* XI (1926). The *Journal of the Medical Society of New Jersey* is a major source of information on the Essex County Society's and the State Society's Committees on Maternal Welfare, and on Dr. Bingham's activities. Later developments are traced in Hammell P. Shipps, "Advances in Maternal Welfare," *Journal of the Medical Society of New Jersey,* L (1953); Walter B. Mount, "Ten Years With the Maternal Welfare Commission of Essex County," in the same *Journal,* XXX (1933); Harold A. Murray, "The Mother's Milk

Bank of Essex County," in the same *Journal*, L (1953); and Robert E. Wright, "The New Born," in the same *Journal*, XXXV (1938).

The section on the aging makes use of Ellis; the *Journal of the Medical Society;* the statutes of New Jersey; the *Report of the Committee on Related Matters of the New Jersey Health and Welfare Conferences*, Mimeo. (May, 1939); *Resources of New Jersey*, Report I from New Jersey for the White House Conference on Aging, June, 1960; the *Eighty-Fourth Annual Report of the Department of Health* (1961); and the *Medical-Surgical Plan of New Jersey 1962 Annual Statement and Report.*

The opening statistics on the mentally disturbed are from Research Bulletin No. 129 and Summary Statistics Reports of the Department of Institutions and Agencies and the *Nineteenth Annual Report of the Essex County Overbrook Hospital 1961*. Information is also used from Emil Frankel, "Mental Hygiene in New Jersey," *Journal of the Medical Society of New Jersey*, XLII (1945); Ellis; George S. Stevenson, "New Jersey's Contribution to Psychiatric Progress," *Journal of the Medical Society of New Jersey*, L (1953); and Maurice G. Kott, "The Post-War Decade, 1946-1956," *Welfare Reporter*, XI (1960). The same issue of the last contains a chronological table of welfare developments in the State that has been used here. The data on psychiatric beds are from the *Hill-Burton State Plan Data . . . January 1, 1963*. Charles P. Jubenville, "A History of the New Jersey State Village for Epileptics at Skillman" (unpublished doctoral dissertation, Rutgers, The State University, 1957) and James D. Eadline, "The Training School at Vineland—A Historical Sketch," *Welfare Reporter*, XI (1960) are the basis of the material on their respective topics. The report of the State Commission on Mental Health was called *Toward Better Mental Health in New Jersey*, Report of the N. J. State Commission Public Health (Princeton, 1961). The Mental State Health Act was Assembly Bill 111 in both the 1963 and 1964 legislatures.

BIBLIOGRAPHICAL NOTES

The "Sources" named above refer only to those actually cited in the text. In addition, the following works
are of significance in the history of medicine in the State.
This list does not intend to repeat what has been cited
under "Sources" but some duplication has been
unavoidable.

New Jersey Medicine

Only one book has appeared on the history of medicine
in the State of New Jersey: Stephen Wickes *History of
Medicine in New Jersey and of Its Medical Men from
the Settlement of the Province to A.D. 1800* (Newark,
1879). A very valuable work, it unfortunately never was
expanded by Wickes to cover the nineteenth century. The
actual "history" covers only some seventy pages. This is
followed by about forty pages of documents, and then
over three hundred pages of biographies of medical men.
There is here a wealth of information, important and
useful as source material.

Two essays on the history of medicine in New Jersey
have appeared as part of a general State history. Both
were by John H. Bradshaw. The first appeared in Irving
S. Kull's *New Jersey A History* (New York, 1930), II, and
the second in William S. Myers' *The Story of New Jersey*
(New York, 1945), II. Neither is an adequate account in
scope or as history.

A separate and long chapter on New Jersey is to be found in Maurice B. Gordon's *Aesculapius Comes to the Colonies* (Ventnor, 1949). It is a useful collection of medical miscellany and no more. A similar piece by Gordon, in which are gathered the items pertaining to medicine in the *New Jersey Archives* newspaper extracts, appeared in the *Bulletin of Medical History,* XVII (1945).

COUNTY HISTORIES

A great deal of material exists on the history of medicine on the county level. Each general county history usually has a section devoted to medicine. In addition, the *Transactions* and then the *Journal* of the Medical Society of New Jersey contain historical accounts of the various counties and the county medical societies. William J. Carrington wrote on the "History of Medicine in Atlantic County Prior to 1880," in 1930, *Journal of the Medical Society of New Jersey,* XX. E. L. B. Godfrey wrote on "The Medical Profession of Camden County" in 1896, *Transactions of the Medical Society of New Jersey 1896;* and Henry B. Decker told the story again more briefly in 1936 in his "Notes on the History of Medical Practice in Camden County," *Journal of the Medical Society of New Jersey,* XXXIII; Robert M. Bateman and Enoch E. Fithian presented a lengthy "History of Medical Men and of the District Medical Society of the County of Cumberland" in 1871, *Transactions, 1871;* Luther M. Halsey presented a "Historical Address" on the District Medical Society of Gloucester County in *Transactions, 1899;* Dr. J. Henry Clark wrote on "The First Fifty Years of the District Society of Essex County," in *Transactions, 1867;* John Blane presented brief biographical sketches of practitioners in Hunterdon County in *Transactions, 1866* and in 1872 wrote a full "History of the District Medical Society for the County of Hunterdon," *Transactions,* 1872; Barclay S. Fuhrmann presented a brief review of the Hunterdon story in 1946 in his

"Hunterdon County: The First Century and a Quarter," *Journal of the Medical Society of New Jersey*, XLIII; Cornelius Shepperd wrote a "History of the District Medical Society of the County of Mercer, with Short Sketches of Some of Its Past Members," *Transactions, 1898;* T. J. Thomason presented "A History of the District Medical Society of the County of Monmouth" in *Transactions, 1871;* Alexander W. Rogers presented a "Historical and Biographical Address" on medicine in Passaic County in *Transactions, 1894;* Thomas Ryerson included a few historical details in his annual report from Sussex County in 1866, *Transactions, 1866,* and Frederick H. Morrison did a "History of Medicine in Sussex County" in 1929, *Journal of the Medical Society of New Jersey,* XXVI; J. C. Johnson also included historical details in his annual report, from Warren County, in 1866, *Transactions, 1866;* and a "historical committee" prepared "A Medical History of the County of Warren 1765-1890," in *Transactions, 1890.*

The sesquicentennial of the New Jersey Society brought forth a great number of county celebrations and historical addresses. These are chronicled in the 1916 issue of the *Journal* of the Society, XIII. Along with additional material on Atlantic, Cumberland, Essex, and Monmouth counties, there are presentations by David St. John on "Reminiscences of Some of the Older Physicians" of Bergen County; by Luther M. Halsey on "Reminiscences of Gloucester County and Its Practitioners"; by Frank D. Gray on a "Sketch of Hudson County's Medical Past"; by David C. English, "Historical Address on Middlesex County"; by Abraham E. Carpenter, "Historical Address on Morris County"; by Walter B. Johnson on "Reminiscences of Members of the Passaic County Medical Society"; and by J. Hervey Buchanan on two historical addresses on Somerset County.

In addition, county medical histories appeared in other periodicals. "Old Time Bergen County Doctors" by Byron G. Van Horne appeared in the *Papers and Proceedings of the Bergen County Historical Society,* 1906-

1907, No. 3. Joseph Parrish's "Historical Address" on Burlington County before the Medical Society of that county was published in the *Country Practitioner*, I, No. 2 (1879). "Medical Men of Early Times in Cape May" by Julius Way appeared in the *Cape May County Magazine of History and Genealogy*, I, Nos. 4, 5 (1934-1935).

There were also several separate publications of county medical histories. J. B. Somers issued a pamphlet on *The Medical History of Atlantic County, N.J.* (Philadelphia, 1882). Camden County has been especially well covered. John R. Stevenson published the very useful *History of Medicine and Medical Men of Camden County* in Philadelphia in 1886. Godfrey's selection mentioned above was taken from his book by the same name published in Philadelphia in 1896, and the Camden County Medical Society has recently issued a *History of Camden County Medical Society, the Hospitals of Camden County and biographical sketches of the Society members past and present* (Camden, 1957). Clark's work on Essex County, Bateman's on Cumberland, and Blane's on Hunterdon were all reissued in Newark as separates in 1867, 1871, and 1872 respectively. Finally, A. M. Stackhouse wrote on *Maladies, Remedies and Physicians of Colonial Days in Burlington County* (Moorestown, 1908).

All of these county histories are of the same genre. None is the work of a professional historian and all are mainly given up to a collection of documents and biographical sketches. The portions designated as history are usually disjointed anecdotal chronologies and little more. All of them are sources of information of varying significance to the historian.

PERIODICAL LITERATURE ON STATE MEDICAL HISTORY

There is a considerable body of periodical literature on the history of medicine in New Jersey. What follows makes no pretense at being complete. The annual bibliography of American medical history which has appeared in the *Bulletin of the History of Medicine* since 1944 includes New Jersey and offers an excellent guide to the literature since then. One of the earliest articles on New Jersey's medical history was J. B. Munn's "History of the Medical Society of New Jersey" that appeared in the first volume of the *New Jersey Medical Reporter* in 1848. It was mainly an account of the Society's legislative and organizational history. Next was William Pierson's "Historical Narrative," published in the *Transactions* of the State Society in 1866. It was essentially a chronology of the first hundred years of the Society's history. Wickes in 1881 presented "A Twenty Five Years' Review," *Transactions, 1881,* which took the history of the Society a bit further. The best nineteenth-century account, with some attempt at synthesis and topical arrangement, was D. C. English's "Our Medical Society," in the *Transactions, 1895.*

A good deal more has been done on the State Society. Elias J. Marsh gave "An Outline History" of the Society to 1903 in the *Proceedings of The New Jersey Historical Society,* LX (1942). An article by Frank Overton on "The First Decade of the Medical Society of New Jersey," *Journal of the Medical Society of New Jersey,* XXXIII (1936) contains a great deal more information than its title suggests. George H. Lathrope's "Dissertation on the State of Physick in the Colony of New Jersey," *Journal of the Medical Society of New Jersey,* XXVII (1930) is more logically arranged than Wickes, on which it is based. Lancelot Ely's "The Evolution of the Medical Society of New Jersey," *Journal of the Medical Society of New Jersey,* XXXII (1935) is another collection of miscellany. The best brief treatment of this early period, however, is Fred B. Rogers' "The Medical Society of New Jersey—Its First Quarter of a Century," *Journal of the Medical Society of New Jersey,* L (1953). Rogers' "Opifer per orbem dictor," the motto of the Society, *Journal of the Medical Society of New Jersey,* LI (1954) is another of his scholarly contributions to the history of the early years of the Society. Finally, an anonymous article, "1766-1941 The Medical Society of New Jersey," *Journal of the Medical Society of New Jersey*, XXXVIII (1941) gives a rapid overview of the history of the Society. It must be used with caution since it does contain inaccuracies.

The 1916 volume of the *Journal of the Medical Society* is especially valuable for the great amount of memorabilia and reminiscences it contains, profusely illustrated. Besides the county histories already described it is replete with biographies and portraits of New Jersey physicians.

Other articles of some importance to the history of medicine in the State included Josiah C. Trent's "An Early New Jersey Medical License" in the *Bulletin of the History of Medicine*, XV (1944) and Joseph A. Vasselli's "A Pestilence Census-Taker in New Jersey" in the same *Bulletin*, XXV (1951). The last requires an additional word—it was the only utilization of the wealth of material in the published reports of the county correspondents to the State Society for the study of the medical knowledge and practice of the time. It should be noted that Vasselli used data at ten year intervals—his dates are therefore illustrative and must not be thought of as "firsts."

PERIODICAL LITERATURE OF THE TWENTIETH CENTURY

The fiftieth anniversary of the *Journal of the Medical Society of New Jersey* and of the *Academy of Medicine of New Jersey* brought forth a goodly number of historical articles of considerable significance. These appeared in Volume L (1953) of the *Journal,* and in the June, 1961 issue, VII, of the *Academy of Medicine of New Jersey Bulletin.* Among them were the articles by Lathrope, Gerendasy, Goodman, D'Alessandro, Saffron, and Bernhard, cited under Sources. In addition, they included Henry A. Brodkin's "The Military Role of New Jersey Physicians in the Past Fifty Years" in the *Journal,* and Thomas J. White's "New Jersey Medicine—Fifty

Years," and William B. Nevius' "Fifty Years of Pediatrics in New Jersey" in the *Bulletin,* as well as others to be noted below. These articles for the most part summarized the personal knowledge and experience of the writers. They show various degrees of intensity in research, but they are all nevertheless very pertinent accounts by competent witnesses.

SURGERY

There has been no connected study of the history of surgery in New Jersey, but three articles are significant in this connection. One was Edward J. Ill's "An Attempt to Show What New Jersey Surgeons Have Done in Abdominal Surgery" in the *Transactions* of the Medical Society for 1891. A second was David B. Allman's "Fifty Years of Surgical Progress" in the Society's *Journal* of 1953, and Christopher A. Beling's "Fifty Years of Surgery in New Jersey" in the *Academy of Medicine of New Jersey Bulletin,* VII (1961). The last is particularly valuable and has been heavily drawn upon in this book. All three, however, reflect the personal knowledge and experience of the writers and are prone to a parochialism that is unintentional and to a lack of concern with antecedents.

Henry H. Kessler's "Rehabilitation in New Jersey" in the *Journal of the Medical Society of New Jersey,* L (1953) reviews the history of that activity in the State. It is written from the vantage point of a major figure in the field.

EDUCATION

William F. Norwood's *Medical Education in the United States* (Philadelphia, 1944) includes references to New Jersey. Fred B. Rogers' two articles on medical degrees in the State, *Journal of the Medical Society of New Jersey,* L (1953) and LIII (1956), and his related

"Early Medical Schools of New Jersey," *Journal of the Medical Society of New Jersey*, XLIX (1952) are also of significance here. David L. Cowen has written "Notes on Pharmaceutical Training in New Jersey before 1900" in the *American Journal of Pharmaceutical Education*, XII (1948).

SANITATION AND PUBLIC HEALTH

Annual reports of the State Department of Health and its precedent agencies have been published since 1874. These are veritable mines of information and this book has done little more than surface mining. There has also been published since 1915 by the State Department, the *Public Health News*, another source of information hardly tapped by the historian. A third source is the annual *Transactions* of the New Jersey Sanitary Association and its successor organizations that were published from 1895 to 1934.

There are several studies pertaining to the history of public health in New Jersey. D. C. Bowen wrote a short account of the "Health Department in New Jersey" in 1931, *Journal of the Medical Society of New Jersey*, XXXVIII. Daniel Bergsma wrote "Fifty Years of Public Health" in the *Journal* of the State Medical Society, L (1953). It recounts major accomplishments but does not go deeply into any one aspect. J. Bennett Morrison in "An Historical Sketch of the Development of Preventive Medicine in the State of New Jersey," *Journal of the Medical Society of New Jersey*, XXVIII (1931), offered a rapid chronology of the history of medicine in the State with particular emphasis, in the late nineteenth century and after, on health laws and regulations.

There has been no overall study of the history of water and sewerage in the State. Daniel Jacobsen's "The Pollution Problem of the Passaic River" in the *Proceedings of The New Jersey Historical Society*, LXXVI (1958) has shown that there is significant work to be done.

The history of dentists in New Jersey has been the interest of Milton D. Asbell. He has edited *The Southern Dental Society of the State of New Jersey 1899-1949 A History of Dentistry in South Jersey* (n.p., 1949). It contains some interesting historical material but the bulk of it is biographical. He has also written "A Brief Sketch of New Jersey's Contribution to Licensure in Dentistry" in the *Journal of the New Jersey State Dental Society*, XXV, No. 2 (1953); and "Historical Notes on Dentistry in South Jersey," in the *Southern Dental Society of New Jersey Outlook and Bulletin*, XXIX (1960).

Woodrow S. Monica has written on "Fifty Years of Dentistry in New Jersey" in the *Academy of Medicine of New Jersey Bulletin*, VII, No. 2 (1961).

A History of the New Jersey State Dental Society was published in 1931 by a committee of that Society of which John C. Forsyth was chairman. It is a chronological account of the highlights of each annual convention and contains a great deal of information. The history of "The New Jersey Pharmaceutical Association, 1870-1945" has been written by David L. Cowen in the *New Jersey Journal of Pharmacy*, XVIII (1945). He has also written on "New Jersey Pharmacy and American History," in the *Journal of the American Pharmaceutical Association* (Pract. Ed., X, 1949).

PROFESSIONAL JOURNALS

The first professional journal of substance in New Jersey was the *New Jersey Medical Reporter, and Transactions of the New Jersey Medical Society* that was established by Joseph Parrish at Burlington in 1847. In 1859 it dropped its publication of the transactions and in 1864 it left New Jersey for Philadelphia, where it became the *Medical and Surgical Reporter*. In 1859 the Medical Society of New Jersey itself began to publish its *Trans-*

actions annually. However, the Society decided to publish all of its transactions going back to the beginnings, so that there are now published transactions from 1766 to 1903. The monthly publication of the *Journal of the Medical Society of New Jersey* was begun in 1904. This represents the longest run of such proceedings of any group in organized medicine in the country. *The Country Practitioner, or, New Jersey Journal of Medical & Surgical Practice* was established by Dr. E. P. Townsend at Beverly in 1879. It was a sharply written journal but, although it seemed to be thriving, came to an abrupt end within two years.

A *New Jersey Eclectic Medical and Surgical Journal* was published in the State from 1874 to 1876 when it moved to New York and then westward, changing its name each time. The Eclectic Medical Society of the State of New Jersey published its *Transactions* in 1876 and 1877 at least.

The New Jersey State Homeopathic Medical Society is recorded as having published *Transactions* or *Proceedings* from 1855 to 1911, but very few of these are known to exist. Still another New Jersey journal—actually the earliest medical periodical in the State—was *The Fountain or Hydropathic Journal* published at Morristown in 1846.

The New Jersey Association of Osteopathic Physicians and Surgeons has issued a *Bulletin* since its organization in 1901. In 1963 it became the *Journal* of the Association.

The New Jersey State Dental Society has published *Transactions* or *Proceedings* since 1870. It issued a *New Jersey Dental Journal* from 1912 to 1919, and has issued the current *Journal of the New Jersey State Dental Society* since 1929.

The published *Proceedings of the New Jersey Pharmaceutical Association* begin with its origin in 1870 and have been continuous until the commencement of its *New Jersey Journal of Pharmacy* in 1928. It is now a monthly publication.

INDEX

Commando, Harry N., 123
Commonwealth Fund, 140
Comte, Auguste, 53
Condict, Lewis, 29, 31
Connecticut, 13, 15
Contagion, 25-27, 37-38, 43, 86, 89
Cooper, Richard M., 93
Cornwall, Lord, 13
Corson, John W., 65
Country Practitioner, 28, 34, 36, 38, 46, 47, 60, 68
County Medical Societies, *see* Medical Societies, District
Crecca, Anthony D., 126
Crecca, Joseph V., 126
Crosswicks, 4
Cuba, 166
Cullen, William, 20, 22, 48
Culpeper, Nicholas, 7, 18, 19
Culver, J. E., 37
Cumberland County, 35, 88, 105
Currie, D. A., 47
Cutter, James B., 62

Dairies, 161, 162, 182
Dandy, Walter, 124
Danzis, Max, 127
Dartmouth College, 75
Davidson, Henry A., 116
Dayton, A. B., 28, 53
Deaf, 102
Decker, Henry B., 135
Degenerative diseases, 120
Deibert, Irvin E., 126
Dental publications, 212
Dental research, 143
Dental Schools, 133, 135, 136, 143. *See also* Seton Hall *and* Fairleigh Dickinson Universities
Dentistry, 37, 128-129, 132, 137-139, 211. *See also* Tooth extraction
Devonish, Bernard, 5
De Wildey, John, 18
Dexter, George T., 72

Diabetes, 55, 56, 57, 113, 175
Diagnosis, diagnostic tests and instruments, 39, 53-57, 108, 114-117, 147, 149, 154
Dickinson, Jonathan, 6, 21
Dioscorides, 18
Diphtheria, 2, 4, 21, 28, 43-45, 47-49, 79, 80, 82, 108, 110, 114, 117, 161, 182
Diphtheria antitoxin, 45, 108, 114, 117
Disease and Diseases, 2-4, 15, 17, 20-22, 25-27, 28, 29, 31, 33, 37, 40-46, 48, 49, 56-58, 64, 79, 107-110, 113-115, 117-120, 142, 144, 152, 154, 163, 165, 166, 169, 175, 180, 182. *See also* Fevers *and* individual diseases
Disease identification, 28
Disease, theories of, *see* Germ theory, Medical theory, Theory of disease
Dispensaries, 88, 92, 93, 98, 169
Dispensatories and Pharmacopoeias, 4, 18-19, 48
Dissection, 9, 56, 59, 76
District of Columbia, 106
District Medical Societies, *see* Medical Societies, District
District physicians, 169
Dix, Dorothea Lynde, 101-103
Doctor (title), 5-6
Domestic Medicine, 3-5, 44
Dougherty, Alexander N., 56, 57
Driscoll, Alfred E., 136
Drug industry, *see* Pharmaceutical manufacturers
Drug stores, 5
Drugs, *see* Materia medica
Duyckinck, G., 5

Eagleton, Wells P., 126, 127, 129
Eagleton technic, 126

East Orange, 110, 172
Eclecticism, 71-75, 127, 129, 212
Edinburgh, University of, 8, 22
Edwards, A. M., 57
Ehrenberg, Christian C., 36
Ehrlich, Paul, 113-115, 119
Eliot, Charles, 77
Eliot, Jared, 15
Elizabeth, Elizabethtown, 3, 6, 9, 81, 83, 91, 97n., 109, 167, 168
Elmer, Jonathan, 8
Elmer, Moses G., 19-20
Emergency Relief Administration, 157
Emetics, 29, 32, 45
Encephalitis, 163, 169
Enzymes, 142, 143
Epidemiological Society of London, 88
Epidemiology, 87, 112
Epileptics, 178
Episcopalians and hospitals, 95, 97n., 100
Ergot, 49, 50, 56
Essex County, 25, 43, 56, 97, 104, 156, 173, 176-178
Essex County Child Guidance Center, 178
Essex County Heart Association, 152
Essex County Juvenile Clinic, 178
Essex County Medical Commission for Maternal Welfare, 172
Essex County Service for the Chronically Ill, 175
Essexfields, 178
Ether, *see* Anesthetics

Fairleigh Dickinson University: Nursing program, 134; School of Dentistry, 139, 143

Fees and fee bills, 11, 19, 21, 68-69, 160, 170-171
Fevers and agues, 2, 26, 28, 31, 32, 40, 43, 46, 109. *See also* individual diseases
Flemington, 154
Flexner, Simon, 122
Flexner Report, 76, 128
Flexner vaccine, 115
Folk medicine, 3-4, 46-47
Force, Benjamin, 20
Fort Lee, 91
Fountain or Hydropathic Journal, 72
France, 36, 43, 49, 54, 55, 103
Franklin, William, 14
Freeborn, G. C., 57
Freehold, 14
Freeman, I. Addison, 58

Galen, 18, 20
Garrison, S. Olin, 178
Gastroenterology, 122, 123
Geriatrics, 58, 120
Germ theory of disease, 26, 27, 36-39, 79, 89, 112
Germany, 47, 48, 55, 56, 178
Gervals (Gervais), John M., 97
Gesner, Conrad, 48
Gilbert, Lawrence, 126
Glasgow, University of, 75
Glen Gardner, 118
Gloucester, 9, 27, 110n.
Gloucester County, 27, 35, 47, 72, 97, 105
Goble, J. G., 29
Goddard, H. H., 178
Goldstone, Karl H., 117
Goodman, Prof., 31
Gordon, Charles, 1
Gordon, George, 9
Gordon, John, 1
Grave robbing, 9
Great Britain, 1, 5-7, 11, 13, 36, 48, 54, 57, 65, 80, 123
Greenland, Henry, 5
Gross, S. D., 36

Medical ethics and professionalism, 11-12, 14, 157, 160
Medical instruments and equipment, 19, 21, 53-56, 64, 114-115, 149, 182
Medical libraries, 59, 122
Medical museum, 59
Medical practice and practitioners, 5-7, 19-23, 33, 71-74, 116
Medical publications, 59-60, 117, 121, 122, 127, 151, 211-212
Medical Record, 55
Medical Repository, 47
Medical research, 52-53, 136, 140-145, 152-154
Medical Schools, 7, 8, 67, 69, 71-73, 75-77, 98, 110, 121, 123, 128, 130, 133, 135-140, 143, 149; Central University of Medicine and Surgery, 77; College of Philadelphia, 8; Columbia College of Physicians and Surgeons, 57; Eclectic Medical and Surgical College of the State of New Jersey, 77; Eclectic Medical College, 75; Essex Medical College, 135; Geneva Medical College, 76; Hahnemann Medical School, 75; Harvard Medical School, 57, 77; Hygeo-Therapeutic Institute, 77; Jefferson Medical College, 36, 75; Livingston University, 77; Medical and Surgical College of the State of New Jersey, 77; Metropolitan Medical College, 72; New York University – Bellevue School of Medicine, 155; Penn University, 75;

Pennsylvania College, 75; Pennsylvania College of Homeopathic Medicine, 75; Philadelphia College, 75; Philadelphia University, 75; Rutgers Medical College, 76; State University of New York School of Medicine, 155; University of Medicine and Surgery of Haddonfield, 77; University of Pennsylvania School of Medicine, 75, 155. *See also* Rutgers and Seton Hall Universities
Medical Science, 14-17, 52-59, 79, 110-114
Medical services, government programs for, 157, 171, 175-176
Medical Societies: District (County): 58n., 130; Burlington, 56, 59, 68, 69; Camden, 35, 65, 74; Cape May, 58n.; Essex, 47, 59, 172-174; Gloucester, 68; Hudson, 59, 92; Hunterdon, 68-69; Mercer, 54, 59; Monmouth, 59n.; Warren, 31;
Local: Academy of Medicine of Northern New Jersey, 122; Essex County Pathologic and Anatomic Society, 122; Essex Medical Union, 58, 59; Hudson County Pathological Society, 56, 59; Jersey City Pathological Society, 59; Medical Library Association of Newark, 122; Medical Society of the Eastern District of New Jersey, 9; Newark Medical Association, 58n., 68; Orange Mountain Medi-

cal Society, 58n.; Trenton Medical Association, 58n., Trenton Medical Library Association, 122; William Pearson Medical Library Association, 122;

State: Academy of Medicine of New Jersey, 122; Eclectic Medical Society of the State of New Jersey, 72, 212; Medical Society of New Jersey, 6, 7, 10-15, 17, 22, 24, 32, 38, 42, 47, 52, 54, 55, 56, 58-61, 66, 68-70, 74, 76-78, 80, 83, 84, 98, 102, 104, 113, 115, 116, 118, 128, 129, 135, 136, 140, 157, 158, 161, 166, 167, 173, 175, 182; Standing Committee, 24, 25, 32, 35, 40, 41, 50, 52, 53, 61, 62, 66, 75, 91; Medical Society of the State of New Jersey, 10 (see Medical Society of New Jersey); New Jersey Academy of Medicine, 59; New Jersey Academy of General Practice, 122; New Jersey Gastroenterological Society, 122; New Jersey Medical Society, 10 (see Medical Society of New Jersey); New Jersey Society of Osteopathic Physicians and Surgeons, 182, 212; New Jersey State Homeopathic Society, 73, 212

Medical specialization, 64-67, 122, 149, 154, 155

Medical-Surgical Plan of New Jersey, see Blue Shield

Medical technicians, 131, 151

Medical theory, 17-18, 20, 22-23, 28-29, 31-34, 38. See also Germ theory

Medicines, see Materia medica

Mental health, 175, 177, 179

Mentally disturbed and deficient, 176-179

Mercer County, 97

Merck and Company, 144-145

Merck Company Foundation, 140

Mercury, 20, 32, 45, 56, 58. See also Calomel

Meteorology, 26-27

Meyner, Robert, 140

Miasma, 1, 26-27, 37

Micheau, Paul, 9

Michener, E., 29, 35-36

Microbiology, 141. See also Bacteriology

Microscopy, 37, 39, 46, 57, 114

Middle States Reformed Medical Society, 72

Middlesex County, 5, 89, 97

Middletown, 5

Midwives, 172

Milk, certified, 66, 80

Millburn, 58

Miller, Ephraim, 19, 21

Monmouth County, 89

Montclair, 50, 72, 126

Morgagni, Giovanni, 22

Morphine, 46, 49-51

Morris Plains, 105, 145. See also Hospitals, Mental, State, Greystone Park

Morristown, 5, 89-91

Morristown Hydropathic Institution, 72

Morrogh, C., 62

Mortality rates, 41-45, 79, 81-83, 92, 99, 107-110, 117-120, 180. See also Maternal and Neo-natal mortality

Mosquito Extermination Commissions, County, 168

Mosquitoes, 113, 141, 165-169, 182

Mother's Milk Bank, 174

Mt. Kipp, 118
Moynihan, Sir Berkeley, 123

Narcotic addiction, 50-51
National Institutes of Health, 143
National Tuberculosis Association, 118
Neo-natal mortality, 171, 172, 174, 180
New Brunswick, 9, 10, 29, 62, 76, 91, 97n., 124, 136-138, 144, 149
New Brunswick Microscopical Society, 57
New England, 1
New Haven, 100
New Jersey (State): Aging, Division on, 175; Agricultural Experiment Station, 166-169; Arthur Brisbane Child Treatment Center, 178; Bacteriology Laboratory, 87, 114; Child Hygiene, Bureau of, 171-173; Child Hygiene, Division of, 171; Chronic Illness Control, Division of, 144, 175; Chronic Illness, Governor's Conference on Prevention of, 175; Chronic Sick, Advisory Council on, 175; Dentistry, State Board of, 128, 135; Diagnostic Center (Menlo Park), 178; Epileptics, State Village of, 178; Health, Board of, 80, 85-87, 107, 161-166, Divisions, 161; Health Commission, 87; Health, Commissioner of, 162; Health, Department of, 162-163, 165, 171, 173, 175, Divisions, 162-163; Highfields, 178; Institutions and Agencies, Department of, 171, 176; Jamesburg State Home, 177; Lunatics, Commission to ascertain to number of, 102; Lunatics, Joint Committee on asylum for, 102; Maternal and Child Health, Bureau of, 173; Medical College Commission, 136-137, 139; Medical Examiners, Board of, 71, 73-74, 77, 128, 129, 131, 132, 135; Mental Health; Commission on, 179; Mosquito Control Commission, 168; Mosquito Control Study Commission, 168; Neuro-Psychiatric Institute, 178; Nurses, Board of Examiners of, 132, 133; Nursing, Board of, 132; Optometry, Board of, 132; Pharmacy, Board of, 129; Public Health Council, 162; Public Medical Care, Commission to Study the Administration of, 170; Quarantine Service, 89; Rehabilitation Commission, 152n.; Sanatorium for Chest Diseases (Glen Gardner), 118; Sanitary Commission, 84-85, 87, 88; Sewerage Commission, 161, 164; Skillman State Village, 178; State Hospitals, see Hospitals, Mental; Vital Statistics, Bureau of, 87 (see also Vital Statistics); Water Policy and Supply Council, 165; Water Policy Commission, 165; Water Supply Commission, 165; Welfare, Division of, 171
New Jersey Association for the Relief and Prevention of Tuberculosis, 118

Parkeville Hydropathic Institute, 72
Parrish, Joseph, 58, 60
Passaic, 82
Passaic County, 97, 105
Passaic River, 82-83
Passaic Valley Sewerage Commission, 164
Pasteur, Louis, 37, 38
Patent medicines, 5
Paterson, 64, 67, 88, 89, 94, 95, 109, 110n., 126
Pathologic anatomy, 22, 33, 35, 64
Pathology, 33, 56, 57, 59, 60, 122, 143
Pediatrics, 66, 127, 146, 154, 174
Peer, Lyndon A., 127
Pelletier, P. J., 49
Penicillin, 119-120, 144
Pennington, William, 102, 106
Pennsylvania, 2, 76, 89
Percussion, 53-54, 117
Perth Amboy, 7, 9, 89, 91
Pharmaceutical manufacturers, 144-145
Pharmaceutical publications, 212
Pharmacology, 48, 56, 60, 120, 134
Pharmacopoeia, see Dispensatories
Pharmacy and Pharmaceutical education, 2, 18, 129, 132, 134-135, 137, 211, 212
Philadelphia, 2, 3, 8, 9, 36, 41, 42, 60, 64, 66, 69, 71, 81, 82, 83, 100, 133, 147, 180
Philadelphia Dispensary, 29
Phlebotomy, see Venesection
Physiology, 46, 48, 56, 60, 101, 112, 142, 143
Pierson, Abraham, 6n.
Pierson, William, 49, 65
Pinel, Philippe, 103
Pinkham, J. W., 50
Pitkin, George P., 127

Pneumonia, 31, 43, 47, 49, 54, 120
Premedical education, 12, 77-78, 121, 128
Prenatal care, 154, 172, 174
Preventive medicine, 79, 84, 154, 163, 181
Princeton, 143
Princeton University, 136, 142. See also College of New Jersey
Providence, 81, 88
Psychiatry and psychiatric services, 58, 104, 105, 112, 146, 177-179
Public Health, 161-169, 210
Public Health News, 163
Public Welfare, 166-176. See also Sick-poor
Puerperal fever, 60-61
Purging, 19, 20, 23, 29, 31-34, 45

Quackery and Sectarianism, 2, 12, 21, 69, 71-75, 129-132
Quarantine, 2, 81, 84, 86, 88-90
Queen's College, 9, 76
Quincy, John, 19
Quinine, 35, 45, 49, 50, 56

Radioactivity, 149, 152
Radioisotopes, 149
Rahway River Sewerage Authority, 164
Reading, 3
Referendum of 1954, 137
Rehabilitation, 152-154, 175, 179
Residencies, 98, 130, 136, 147, 149, 151, 177
Revolutionary War, 4, 8, 91
Rheims, University of, 8
Rhode Island, 13, 101, 110
Richmond, 81
Roberts, John, 18
Robinson, Morton, 72, 77
Robinson, William, 9

Sprague, Edward W., 124, 126, 158
Squibb, E. R. & Sons, 144
Stanley, Wendell M., 143
State Charities Aid Association of New Jersey, 118
Staten Island, 165
Statistics, medical, 3, 36. See Mortality rates
Stevenson, John R., 40, 58
Sthenic diseases, 22-23, 32-33, 35
Stickler, Dr., 39
Streptomycin, 118, 119, 120, 141, 144
Sulfonamides, 119
Surgery, 2, 5, 11, 13-14, 21, 22, 45, 60-66, 98, 101, 112, 114, 123-127, 130, 131, 142, 149, 154, 209
Sussex County, 31, 88, 97, 147
Swain, Richard D., 123
Swan, James, 70
Swedish settlements, 2
Sweet, Jonathan R., 77
Sydenham, Thomas, 17, 18, 20, 22

Takamine, Jôkichi, 115
Talbot, Robert, 16, 18
Teimer, Theodore, 172
Theory of disease, see Medical theory
Therapeutic nihilism, 33-34
Therapeutics, 3, 4, 19-21, 23, 29, 31-36, 39, 45-51, 57, 72, 74, 79, 115, 116, 119, 120, 130, 148. See also Emetics, Materia medica, Purging, Venesection
Thomsonianism, 33, 71, 72
Thornton, Samuel C., 49
Tissue committees, 149
Tooth extraction, 11, 21, 55
Town physicians, 86, 169
Townsend, E. P., 60
Trager, William, 143
Transactions of the Medical

Society of New Jersey, 24, 30, 55, 60, 116
Trenton, 5, 8, 42, 67, 68, 81, 91, 95, 104, 109, 110, 156. See also Hospitals, Mental, State
Tuberculosis, 41, 43, 108, 109, 113, 114, 117-120, 141, 146
Turrell, 178
Typhoid fever 2, 27, 28, 40, 41, 79, 81-83, 96, 108, 109, 114, 117

Union, 130
Union County, 81, 97
University of the State of New Jersey, 135
Urbanization, 52, 81, 109-110, 182
Urology, 127

Vaccination, 22, 42, 79, 84, 86, 88, 93, 108
Vaccines, 79, 112, 113, 115, 117, 161
Vail, M. H. C., 66
Vandeveer, Lawrence, 47
Van Riper, C. S., 63, 100
Variolation, 3, 22
Venereal disease, 20, 43, 48, 114, 115
Venesection, 11, 19-21, 23, 29, 31-36, 49
Veratrum viride, 32, 34, 48-49
Verona, 104
Vienna, 33
Vierordt, Karl, 55
Vineland, Training School at, 178
Virginia, 1
Vital Statistics, 85-87, 161, 163. See also Mortality rates

Wade, Nathaniel, 13
Waksman, Selman A., 141, 144
Ward, John, 178
Warner Lambert Pharmaceutical Co., 145